PENGUIN TWENTIETH-CENTURY CLASSICS

THE STORIES OF F. SCOTT FITZGERALD VOLUME 2: THE CRACK-UP WITH OTHER PIECES AND STORIES

F. Scott Fitzgerald was born in 1896 in St Paul, Minnesota, and went to Princeton University which he left in 1917 to join the army. He was said to have epitomized the Jazz Age which he himself defined as 'a generation grown up to find all Gods dead, all wars fought, all faiths in man shaken.' In 1920 he married Zelda Sayre. Their traumatic marriage and subsequent breakdowns became the leading influence in his writing. Among his publications were five novels, *This Side of Paradise*, *The Great Gatsby*, *The Beautiful and Damned*, *Tender is the Night* and *The Last Tycoon* (his last and unfinished work); six volumes of short stories and *The Crack-Up*, a selection of autobiographical pieces. Fitzgerald died suddenly in 1940. After his death *The New York Times* said of him that 'He was better than he knew, for in fact and in the literary sense he invented a "generation" . . . he might have interpreted them and even guided them, as in their middle years they saw a different and nobler freedom threatened with destruction.'

The Stories of F. Scott Fitzgerald

VOLUME 2

THE CRACK-UP

with other Pieces and Stories

PENGUIN BOOKS

PENGUIN BOOKS

Published by the Penguin Group
Penguin Books Ltd, 27 Wrights Lane, London W8 5TZ, England
Viking Penguin, a division of Penguin Books USA Inc.
375 Hudson Street, New York, New York 10014, USA
Penguin Books Australia Ltd, Ringwood, Victoria, Australia
Penguin Books Canada Ltd, 2801 John Street, Markham, Ontario, Canada L3R 1B4
Penguin Books (NZ) Ltd, 182–190 Wairau Road, Auckland 10, New Zealand

Penguin Books Ltd, Registered Offices: Harmondsworth, Middlesex, England

'Echoes of the Jazz Age' first published 1931
'My Lost City' first published 1945
'Ring' first published 1933
'The Crack-Up' first published 1936
'Early Success' first published 1937
'Gretchen's Forty Winks' first published 1924
'The Last of the Belles' first published 1929
'Babylon Revisited' first published 1931
'Pat Hobby Himself' first published 1940
'Financing Finnegan' first published 1938
Published together as Volume 2 of *The Bodley Head Scott Fitzgerald* (1958–63)
Published in Penguin Books 1965
20 19 18 17 16 15 14

Made and printed in Great Britain by
BPCC Hazell Books
Aylesbury, Bucks, England
Member of BPCC Ltd.
Set in Linotype Granjon

Contents

Autobiographical Pieces

Echoes of the Jazz Age

It is too soon to write about the Jazz Age with perspective, and without being suspected of premature arteriosclerosis. Many people still succumb to violent retching when they happen upon any of its characteristic words – words which have since yielded in vividness to the coinages of the underworld. It is as dead as were the Yellow Nineties in 1902. Yet the present writer already looks back to it with nostalgia. It bore him up, flattered him and gave him more money than he had dreamed of, simply for telling people that he felt as they did, that something had to be done with all the nervous energy stored up and unexpended in the War.

The ten-year period that, as if reluctant to die outmoded in its bed, leaped to a spectacular death in October, 1929, began about the time of the May Day riots in 1919. When the police rode down the demobilized country boys gaping at the orators in Madison Square, it was the sort of measure bound to alienate the more intelligent young men from the prevailing order. We didn't remember anything about the Bill of Rights until Mencken began plugging it, but we did know that such tyranny belonged in the jittery little countries of South Europe. If goose-livered business men had this effect on the government, then maybe we had gone to war for J. P. Morgan's loans after all. But, because we were tired of Great Causes, there was no more than a short outbreak of moral indignation, typified by Dos Passos' *Three Soldiers*. Presently we began to have slices of the national cake, and our idealism only flared up when the newspapers made melodrama out of such stories as Harding and the

Ohio Gang or Sacco and Vanzetti. The events of 1919 left us cynical rather than revolutionary, in spite of the fact that now we are all rummaging around in our trunks wondering where in hell we left the liberty cap – 'I know I *had* it' – and the moujik blouse. It was characteristic of the Jazz Age that it had no interest in politics at all.

It was an age of miracles, it was an age of art, it was an age of excess, and it was an age of satire. A Stuffed Shirt, squirming to blackmail in a lifelike way, sat upon the throne of the United States; a stylish young man hurried over to represent to us the throne of England. A world of girls yearned for the young Englishman; the old American groaned in his sleep as he waited to be poisoned by his wife, upon the advice of the female Rasputin who then made the ultimate decision in our national affairs. But such matters apart, we had things our way at last. With Americans ordering suits by the gross in London, the Bond Street tailors perforce agreed to moderate their cut to the American long-waisted figure and loose-fitting taste, something subtle passed to America, the style of man. During the Renaissance Francis the First looked to Florence to trim his leg. Seventeenth-century England aped the court of France, and fifty years ago the German Guards officer bought his civilian clothes in London. Gentlemen's clothes – symbol of 'the power that man must hold and that passes from race to race'.

We were the most powerful nation. Who could tell us any longer what was fashionable and what was fun? Isolated during the European War, we had begun combing the unknown South and West for folkways and pastimes, and there were more ready to hand.

The first social revelation created a sensation out of all proportion to its novelty. As far back as 1915 the unchaperoned young people of the smaller cities had discovered the mobile privacy of that automobile given to young Bill at sixteen to make him 'self-reliant'. At first petting was a desperate adventure even under such favourable conditions, but presently confidences were exchanged and the old commandment broke down. As early as 1917 there were references to such sweet and casual dalliance in any number of the *Yale Record* or the *Princeton Tiger*.

But petting in its more audacious manifestations was confined to the wealthier classes – among other young people the old standard prevailed until after the War, and a kiss meant that a proposal was expected, as young officers in strange cities sometimes discovered to their dismay. Only in 1920 did the veil finally fall – the Jazz Age was in flower.

Scarcely had the staider citizens of the republic caught their breaths when the wildest of all generations, the generation which had been adolescent during the confusion of the War, brusquely shouldered my contemporaries out of the way and danced into the limelight. This was the generation whose girls dramatized themselves as flappers, the generation that corrupted its elders and eventually overreached itself less through lack of morals than through lack of taste. May one offer in exhibit the year 1922! That was the peak of the younger generation, for though the Jazz Age continued, it became less and less an affair of youth.

The sequel was like a children's party taken over by the elders, leaving the children puzzled and rather neglected and rather taken aback. By 1923 their elders, tired of watching the carnival with ill-concealed envy, had discovered that young liquor will take the place of young blood, and with a whoop the orgy began. The younger generation was starred no longer.

A whole race going hedonistic, deciding on pleasure. The precocious intimacies of the younger generation would have come about with or without prohibition – they were implicit in the attempt to adapt English customs to American conditions. (Our South, for example, is tropical and early maturing – it has never been part of the wisdom of France and Spain to let young girls go unchaperoned at sixteen and seventeen.) But the general decision to be amused that began with the cocktail parties of 1921 had more complicated origins.

The word jazz in its progress towards respectability has meant first sex, then dancing, then music. It is associated with a state of nervous stimulation, not unlike that of big cities behind the lines of a war. To many English the War still goes on because all the forces that menace them are still active – Wherefore eat, drink and be merry, for tomorrow we die. But different causes had now brought about a corresponding state in America – though there were entire classes (people over fifty, for example) who spent a whole decade denying its existence even when its puckish face peered into the family circle. Never did they dream that they had contributed to it. The honest citizens of every class, who believed in a strict public morality and were powerful enough to enforce the necessary legislation, did not know that they would necessarily be served by criminals and quacks, and do not really believe it today. Rich righteousness had always been able to buy honest and intelligent servants to free the slaves or the Cubans, so when this attempt collapsed our elders stood firm with all the stubbornness of people involved in a weak case, preserving their righteousness and losing their children. Silver-haired women and men with fine old faces, people who never did a consciously dishonest thing in their lives, still assure each other in the apartment hotels of New York and Boston and Washington that 'there's a whole generation growing up that will never know the taste of liquor'. Meanwhile their granddaughters pass the well-thumbed copy of *Lady Chatterley's Lover* around the boarding-school and, if they get about at all, know the taste of gin or corn at sixteen. But the generation who reached maturity between 1875 and 1895 continued to believe what they want to believe.

Even the intervening generations were incredulous. In 1920 Heywood Broun announced that all this hubbub was nonsense, that young men didn't kiss but told anyhow. But very shortly people over twenty-five came in for an intensive education. Let me trace some of the revelations vouchsafed them by reference to a dozen works written for various types of mentality during the decade. We begin with the suggestion that Don Juan leads an interesting life (*Jurgen*, 1919); then we learn that there's a lot of sex around if we only knew it (*Winesburg, Ohio*, 1920), that adolescents lead very amorous lives (*This Side of Paradise*, 1920), that there are a lot of neglected Anglo-Saxon words (*Ulysses*, 1921), that older people don't always resist sudden temptations (*Cytherea*, 1922), that girls are sometimes seduced without being ruined (*Flaming Youth*, 1922), that even rape often turns out well (*The Sheik*, 1922), that glamorous English ladies are often promiscuous (*The Green Hat*, 1924), that in fact they devote most of their time to it (*The Vortex*, 1926), that it's a damn good thing too (*Lady Chatterley's Lover*, 1928), and finally that there are abnormal variations (*The Well of Loneliness*, 1928, and *Sodom and Gomorrah*, 1929).

In my opinion the erotic element in these works, even *The Sheik* written for children in the key of *Peter Rabbit*, did not one particle of harm. Everything they described, and much more, was familiar in our contemporary life. The majority of the theses were honest and elucidating – their effect was to restore some dignity to the male as opposed to the he-man in American life. ('And what is a "He-man"?' demanded Gertrude Stein one day. 'Isn't it a large enough order to fill out to the dimensions of all that "a man" has meant in the past? A "*He*-man"!') The married woman can now discover whether she is being cheated, or whether sex is just something to be endured, and her compensation should be to establish a tyranny of the spirit, as her mother may have hinted. Perhaps many women found that love was meant to be fun. Anyhow the objectors lost their tawdry little case, which is one reason why our literature is now the most living in the world.

Contrary to popular opinion, the movies of the Jazz Age had no effect upon its morals. The social attitude of the producers was timid, behind the times, and banal – for example, no picture mirrored even faintly the younger generation until 1923, when magazines had already been started to celebrate it and it had long ceased to be news. There were a few feeble splutters and then Clara Bow in *Flaming Youth*; promptly the Hollywood hacks ran the theme into its cinematographic grave. Throughout the Jazz Age the movies got no farther than Mrs Jiggs, keeping up with its most blatant superficialities. This was no doubt due to the censorship as well as to innate conditions in the industry. In any case, the Jazz Age now raced along under its own power, served by great filling stations full of money.

The people over thirty, the people all the way up to fifty, had joined the dance. We greybeards (to tread down F.P.A.) remember the uproar when in 1912 grandmothers of forty tossed away their crutches and took lessons in the Tango and the Castle-Walk. A dozen years later a woman might pack the Green Hat with her other affairs as she set off for Europe or New York, but Savonarola was too busy flogging dead horses in Augean stables of his own creation to notice. Society, even in small cities, now dined in separate chambers, and the sober table learned about the gay table only from hearsay. There were very few people left at the sober table. One of its former glories, the less sought-after girls who had become resigned to sublimating a probable celibacy, came across Freud and Jung in seeking their intellectual recompense and came tearing back into the fray.

By 1926 the universal preoccupation with sex had become a nuisance. (I remember a perfectly mated, contented young mother asking my wife's advice about 'having an affair right away', though she had no one especially in mind, 'because don't you think it's sort of undignified when you get much over thirty?') For a while bootleg Negro records with their phallic euphemisms made everything suggestive, and simultaneously came a wave of erotic plays – young girls from finishing-schools packed the galleries to hear about the romance of being a Lesbian and George Jean Nathan protested. Then one young producer lost his head entirely, drank a beauty's alcoholic bath-water and went to the penitentiary. Somehow his pathetic attempt at romance belongs to the Jazz Age, while his contemporary in prison, Ruth Snyder, had to be hoisted into it by the tabloids – she was, as *The Daily News* hinted deliciously to gourmets, about 'to cook, *and sizzle*, *AND FRY!*' in the electric chair.

The gay elements of society had divided into two main streams, one flowing towards Palm Beach and Deauville, and the other, much smaller, towards the summer Riviera. One could get away with more on the summer Riviera, and whatever happened seemed to have something to do with art. From 1926 to 1929, the great years of the Cap d'Antibes, this corner of France was dominated by a group quite distinct from that American society which is dominated by Europeans. Pretty much of anything went at Antibes – by 1929, at the most gorgeous paradise for swimmers on the Mediterranean no one swam any more, save for a short hang-over dip at noon. There was a picturesque graduation of steep rocks over the sea and somebody's valet and an occasional English girl used to dive from them, but the Americans were content to discuss each other in the bar. This was indicative of something that was taking place in the homeland – Americans were getting soft. There were signs everywhere: we still won the Olympic games but with champions whose names had few vowels in them – teams composed, like the fighting Irish combination of Notre Dame, of fresh overseas blood. Once the French became really interested, the Davis Cup gravitated automatically to their intensity in competition. The vacant lots of the Middle-Western cities were built up now – except for a short period in school, we were not turning out to be an athletic people like the British, after all. The hare and the tortoise. Of course if we wanted to we could be in a minute; we still had all those reserves of ancestral vitality, but one day in 1926 we looked down and found we had flabby arms and a fat pot and couldn't say boop-boop-a-doop to a Sicilian. Shades of Van Bibber! – no Utopian ideal, God knows. Even golf, once considered an effeminate game, had seemed very strenuous of late – an emasculated form appeared and proved just right.

By 1927 a widespread neurosis began to be evident, faintly signalled, like a nervous beating of the feet, by the popularity of crossword puzzles. I remember a fellow expatriate opening a letter from a mutual friend of ours, urging him to come home and be revitalized by the hardy, bracing qualities of the native soil. It was a strong letter and it affected us both deeply, until we noticed that it was headed from a nerve sanatorium in Pennsylvania.

By this time contemporaries of mine had begun to disappear into the dark maw of violence. A classmate killed his wife and himself on Long Island, another tumbled 'accidently' from a skyscraper in Philadelphia, another purposely from a skyscraper in New York. One was killed in a speak-easy in Chicago; another was beaten to death in a speak-easy in New York and crawled home to the Princeton Club to die; still another had his skull crushed by a maniac's axe in an insane asylum where he was confined. These are not catastrophes that I went out of my way to look for – these were my friends; moreover, these things happened not during the depression but during the boom.

In the spring of '27, something bright and alien flashed across the sky. A young Minnesotan who seemed to have had nothing to do with his generation did a heroic thing, and for a moment people set down their glasses in country clubs and speak-easies and thought of their old best dreams. Maybe there was a way out by flying, maybe our restless blood could find frontiers in the illimitable air. But by that time we were all pretty well committed; and the Jazz Age continued; we would all have one more.

Nevertheless, Americans were wandering ever more widely – friends seemed eternally bound for Russia, Persia, Abyssinia, and Central Africa. And by 1928 Paris had grown suffocating. With each new shipment of Americans spewed up by the boom the quality fell off, until towards the end there was something sinister about the crazy boatloads. They were no longer the simple pa and ma and son and daughter, infinitely superior in their qualities of kindness and curiosity to the corresponding class in Europe, but fantastic neanderthals who believed something, something vague, that you remembered from a very cheap novel. I remember an Italian on a steamer who promenaded the deck in an American Reserve Officer's uniform picking quarrels in broken English with Americans who criticized their own institutions in the bar. I remember a fat Jewess, inlaid with diamonds, who sat behind us at the Russian ballet and said as the curtain rose, 'Thad's luffly, dey ought to baint a bicture of it.' This was low comedy, but it was evident that money and power were falling into the hands of people in comparison with whom the leader of a village Soviet would be a gold-mine of judgement and culture. There were citizens travelling in luxury in 1928 and 1929, who, in the distortion of their new condition, had the human value of Pekingese, bivalves, cretins, goats. I remember the Judge from some New York district who had taken his daughter to see the Bayeux Tapestries and made a scene in the papers advocating their segregation because one scene was immoral. But in those days life was like the race in *Alice in Wonderland*, there was a prize for every one.

The Jazz Age had had a wild youth and a heady middle age. There was the phase of the necking parties, the Leopold-Loeb murder (I remember the time my wife was arrested on Queensborough Bridge on the suspicion of being the 'Bob-haired Bandit') and the John Held Clothes. In the second phase such phenomena as sex and murder became more mature, if much more conventional. Middle age must be served and pyjamas came to the beach to save fat thighs and flabby calves from competition with the one-piece bathing-suit. Finally skirts came down and everything was concealed. Everybody was at scratch now. Let's go –

But it was not to be. Somebody had blundered and the most expensive orgy in history was over.

It ended two years ago,* because the utter confidence which was its essential prop received an enormous jolt, and it didn't take long for the flimsy structure to settle earthward. And after two years the Jazz Age seems as far away as the days before the War. It was borrowed time anyhow – the whole upper tenth of a nation living with the insouciance of grand dukes and the casualness of chorus girls. But moralizing is easy now and it was pleasant to be in one's twenties in such a certain and unworried time. Even when you were broke you didn't worry about money, because it was in such profusion around you. Towards the end one had a struggle to pay one's share; it was almost a favour to accept hospitality that required any travelling. Charm, notoriety, mere good manners weighed more than money as a social asset. This was rather splendid, but things were getting thinner and thinner as the eternal necessary human values tried to spread over all that expansion. Writers were

* 1929.

geniuses on the strength of one respectable book or play; just as during the War officers of four months' experience commanded hundreds of men, so there were now many little fish lording it over great big bowls. In the theatrical world extravagant productions were carried by a few second-rate stars, and so on up the scale into politics, where it was difficult to interest good men in positions of the highest importance and responsibility, importance and responsibility far exceeding that of business executives but which paid only five or six thousand a year.

Now once more the belt is tight and we summon the proper expression of horror as we look back at our wasted youth. Sometimes, though, there is a ghostly rumble among the drums, an asthmatic whisper in the trombones that swings me back into the early twenties when we drank wood alcohol and every day in every way grew better and better, and there was a first abortive shortening of the skirts, and girls all looked alike in sweater dresses, and people you didn't want to know said 'Yes, we have no bananas', and it seemed only a question of a few years before the older people would step aside and let the world be run by those who saw things as they were – and it all seems rosy and romantic to us who were young then, because we will never feel quite so intensely about our surroundings any more.

My Lost City

There was first the ferry boat moving softly from the Jersey shore at dawn – the moment crystallized into my first symbol of New York. Five years later when I was fifteen I went into the city from school to see Ina Claire in *The Quaker Girl* and Gertrude Bryan in *Little Boy Blue*. Confused by my hopeless and melancholy love for them both, I was unable to choose between them – so they blurred into one lovely entity, the girl. She was my second symbol of New York. The ferry boat stood for triumph, the girl for romance. In time I was to achieve some of both, but there was a third symbol that I have lost somewhere, and lost for ever.

I found it on a dark April afternoon after five more years.

'Oh, Bunny,' I yelled. *'Bunny!'*

He did not hear me – my taxi lost him, picked him up again half a block down the street. There were black spots of rain on the sidewalk and I saw him walking briskly through the crowd wearing a tan raincoat over his inevitable brown get-up; I noted with a shock that he was carrying a light cane.

'Bunny!' I called again, and stopped. I was still an undergraduate at Princeton while he had become a New Yorker. This was his afternoon walk, this hurry along with his stick through the gathering rain, and as I was not to meet him for an hour it seemed an intrusion to happen upon him engrossed in his private life. But the taxi kept pace with him and as I continued to watch I was impressed: he was no longer the shy little scholar of Holder Court – he walked with confidence, wrapped in his thoughts and looking straight ahead, and it was obvious that his new background was entirely sufficient to him. I knew that he had an apartment where he lived with three other men, released now from all undergraduate taboos, but there was something else that was nourishing him and I got my first impression of that new thing – the Metropolitan spirit.

Up to this time I had seen only the New York that offered itself for inspection – I was Dick Whittington up from the country gaping at the trained bears, or a youth of the Midi dazzled by the boulevards of Paris. I had come only to stare at the show, though the designers of the Woolworth Building and the Chariot Race Sign, the producers of musical comedies and problem plays, could ask for no more appreciative spectator, for I took the style and glitter of New York even above its own valuation. But I had never accepted any of the practically anonymous invitations to debutante balls that turned up in an undergraduate's mail, perhaps because I felt that no actuality could live up to my conception of New York's splendour. Moreover, she to whom I fatuously referred as 'my girl' was a Middle Westerner, a fact which kept the warm centre of the world out there, so I thought of New York as essentially cynical and heartless – save for one night when she made luminous the Ritz Roof on a brief passage through.

Lately, however, I had definitely lost her and I wanted a man's world, and this sight of Bunny made me see New York as just that. A week before, Monsignor Fay had taken me to the Lafayette where there was spread before us a brilliant flag of food, called an *hors d'oeuvre*, and with it we drank claret that was as brave as Bunny's confident cane – but after all it was a restaurant, and afterwards we would drive back over a bridge into the hinterland. The New York of undergraduate dissipation, of Bustanoby's, Shanley's, Jack's, had become a horror, and though I returned to it, alas, through many an alcoholic mist, I felt each time a betrayal of a persistent idealism. My participance was prurient rather than licentious and scarcely one pleasant memory of it remains from those days; as Ernest Hemingway once remarked, the sole purpose of the cabaret is for unattached men to find complaisant women. All the rest is a wasting of time in bad air.

But that night, in Bunny's apartment, life was mellow and safe, a finer distillation of all that I had come to love at Princeton. The gentle playing of an oboe mingled with city noises from the street outside, which penetrated into the room with difficulty through great barricades of books; only the crisp tearing open of invitations by one man was a discordant note. I had found a third symbol of New York and I began wondering about the rent of such apartments and casting about for the appropriate friends to share one with me.

Fat chance – for the next two years I had as much control over my own destiny as a convict over the cut of his clothes. When I got back to New York in 1919 I was so entangled in life that a period of mellow monasticism in Washington Square was not to be dreamed of. The thing was to make enough money in the advertising business to rent a stuffy apartment for two in the Bronx. The girl concerned had never seen New York but she was wise enough to be rather reluctant. And in a haze of anxiety and unhappiness I passed the four most impressionable months of my life.

New York had all the irridescence of the beginning of the world. The returning troops marched up Fifth Avenue and girls were instinctively drawn east and north towards them – this was the greatest nation and there was gala in the air. As I hovered ghost-like in the Plaza Red Room of a Saturday afternoon, or went to lush and liquid garden parties in the East Sixties or tippled with Princetonians in the Biltmore Bar, I was haunted always by my other life – my drab room in the Bronx, my square foot of the subway, my fixation upon the day's letter from Alabama – would it come and what would it say? – my shabby suits, my poverty, and love. While my friends were launching decently into life I had muscled my inadequate bark into midstream. The gilded youth circling around young Constance Bennett in the Club de Vingt, the classmates in the Yale–Princeton Club whooping up our first after-the-war reunion, the atmosphere of the millionaires' houses that I sometimes frequented – these things were empty for me, though I recognized them as impressive scenery and regretted that I was committed to other romance. The most hilarious luncheon table or the most moony cabaret – it was all the same; from them I returned eagerly to my home on Claremont Avenue – home because there might be a letter waiting outside the door. One by one my great dreams of New York became tainted. The remembered charm of Bunny's apartment faded with the rest when I interviewed a blowsy landlady in Greenwich Village. She told me I could bring girls to the room, and the idea filled me with dismay – why should I want to bring girls to my room? – I had a girl. I wandered through the town of 127th Street, resenting its vibrant life; or else I bought cheap theatre seats at Gray's drugstore and tried to lose myself for a few hours in my old passion for Broadway. I was a failure – mediocre at advertising work and unable to get started as a writer. Hating the city, I got roaring, weeping drunk on my last penny and went home. . . .

. . . Incalculable city. What ensued was only one of a thousand success stories of those gaudy days, but it plays a part in my own movie of New York. When I returned six months later the offices of editors and publishers were open to me, impresarios begged plays, the movies panted for screen material. To my bewilderment, I was adopted, not as a Middle Westerner, not even as a detached observer, but as the archetype of what New York wanted. This statement requires some account of the metropolis in 1920.

There was already the tall white city of today, already the feverish activity of the boom, but there was a general inarticulateness. As much as anyone the columnist F.P.A. guessed the pulse of the individual crowd, but shyly, as one watching from a window. Society and the native arts had not mingled – Ellen Mackay was not yet married to Irving Berlin. Many of Peter Arno's people would have been meaningless to the citizen of 1920, and save for F.P.A.'s column there was no forum for metropolitan urbanity.

Then, for just a moment, the 'younger generation' idea became a fusion of many elements in New York life. People of fifty might pretend there was still a four hundred, or Maxwell Bodenheim might pretend there was a Bohemia worth its paint and pencils – but the blending of the bright, gay, vigorous elements began then, and for the first time there appeared a society a little livelier than the solid-mahogany dinner parties of Emily Price Post. If this society produced the cocktail party, it also evolved Park Avenue wit, and for the first time an educated European could envisage a trip to New York as something more amusing than a gold-trek into a formalized Australian Bush.

For just a moment, before it was demonstrated that I was unable to play the role, I, who knew less of New York than any reporter of six months' standing and less of its society than any hall-room boy in a Ritz stag line, was pushed into the position not only of spokesman for the time but of the typical product of that same moment. I, or rather it was 'we' now, did not know exactly what New York expected of us and found it rather confusing. Within a few months after our embarkation on the Metropolitan venture we scarcely knew any more who we were and we hadn't a notion what we were. A dive into a civic fountain, a casual brush with the law, was enough to get us into the gossip columns, and we were quoted on a variety of subjects we knew nothing about. Actually our 'contacts' included half a dozen unmarried college friends and a few new literary acquaintances – I remember a lonesome Christmas when we had not one friend in the city, nor one house we could go to. Finding no nucleus to which we could cling, we became a small nucleus ourselves and gradually we fitted our disruptive personalities into the contemporary scene of New York. Or rather New York forgot us and let us stay.

This is not an account of the city's changes but of the changes in this writer's feeling for the city. From the confusion of the year 1920 I remember riding on top of a taxicab along deserted Fifth Avenue on a hot Sunday night, and a luncheon in the cool Japanese gardens at the Ritz with the wistful Kay Laurel and George Jean Nathan, and writing all night again and again, and paying too much for minute apartments, and buying magnificent but broken-down cars. The first speak-easies had arrived, the toddle was *passé*, the Montmartre was the smart place to dance and Lillian Tashman's fair hair weaved around the floor among the enliquored college boys. The plays were *Declassée* and *Sacred and Profane Love*, and at the Midnight Frolic you danced elbow to elbow with Marion Davies and perhaps picked out the vivacious Mary Hay in the pony chorus. We thought we were apart from all that; perhaps everyone thinks they are apart from their milieu. We felt like small children in a great bright unexplored barn. Summoned out to Griffith's studio on Long Island, we trembled in the presence of the familiar face of the *Birth of a Nation*; later I realized that behind much of the entertainment that the city poured forth into the nation there were only a lot of rather lost and lonely people. The world of the picture actors was like our own in that it was in New York and not of it. It had little sense of itself and no centre: when I first met Dorothy Gish I had the feeling that we were both standing on the

North Pole and it was snowing. Since then they have found a home but it was not destined to be New York.

When bored we took our city with a Huysmans-like perversity. An afternoon alone in our 'apartment' eating olive sandwiches and drinking a quart of Bushmill's whisky presented by Zoë Atkins, then out into the freshly bewitched city, through strange doors into strange apartments with intermittent swings along in taxis through the soft nights. At last we were one with New York, pulling it after us through every portal. Even now I go into many flats with the sense that I have been there before or in the one above or below – was it the night I tried to disrobe in the *Scandals*, or the night when (as I read with astonishment in the paper next morning) 'Fitzgerald Knocks Officer This Side of Paradise'? Successful scrapping not being among my accomplishments, I tried in vain to reconstruct the sequence of events which led up to this dénouement in Webster Hall. And lastly from that period I remember riding in a taxi one afternoon between very tall buildings under a mauve and rosy sky; I began to bawl because I had everything I wanted and knew I would never be so happy again.

It was typical of our precarious position in New York that when our child was to be born we played safe and went home to St Paul – it seemed inappropriate to bring a baby into all that glamour and loneliness. But in a year we were back and we began doing the same things over again and not liking them so much. We had run through a lot, though we had retained an almost theatrical innocence by preferring the role of the observed to that of the observer. But innocence is no end in itself and as our minds unwillingly matured we began to see New York whole and try to save some of it for the selves we would inevitably become.

It was too late – or too soon. For us the city was inevitably linked up with Bacchic diversions, mild or fantastic. We could organize ourselves only on our return to Long

Island and not always there. We had no incentive to meet the city half way. My first symbol was now a memory, for I knew that triumph is in oneself; my second one had grown commonplace – two of the actresses whom I had worshipped from afar in 1913 had dined in our house. But it filled me with a certain fear that even the third symbol had grown dim – the tranquillity of Bunny's apartment was not to be found in the ever-quickening city. Bunny himself was married, and about to become a father, other friends had gone to Europe, and the bachelors had become cadets of houses larger and more social than ours. By this time we 'knew everybody' – which is to say most of those whom Ralph Barton would draw as in the orchestra on an opening night.

But we were no longer important. The flapper, upon whose activities the popularity of my first books was based, had become *passé* by 1923 – anyhow in the East. I decided to crash Broadway with a play, but Broadway sent its scouts to Atlantic City and quashed the idea in advance, so I felt that, for the moment, the city and I had little to offer each other. I would take the Long Island atmosphere that I had familiarly breathed and materialize it beneath unfamiliar skies.

It was three years before we saw New York again. As the ship glided up the river, the city burst thunderously upon us in the early dusk – the white glacier of lower New York swooping down like a strand of a bridge to rise into uptown New York, a miracle of foamy light suspended by the stars. A band started to play on deck, but the majesty of the city made the march trivial and tinkling. From that moment I knew that New York, however often I might leave it, was home.

The tempo of the city had changed sharply. The uncertainties of 1920 were drowned in a steady golden roar and many of our friends had grown wealthy. But the restlessness of New York in 1927 approached hysteria. The parties were bigger – those of Condé Nast, for example, rivalled in their way the fabled balls of the nineties; the pace was faster – the catering to dissipation set an example to Paris; the shows were broader, the buildings were higher, the morals were looser and the liquor was cheaper; but all these benefits did not really minister to much delight. Young people wore out early – they were hard and languid at twenty-one, and save for Peter Arno none of them contributed anything new; perhaps Peter Arno and his collaborators said everything there was to say about the boom days in New York that couldn't be said by a jazz band. Many people who were not alcoholics were lit up four days out of seven, and frayed nerves were strewn everywhere; groups were held together by a generic nervousness and the hang-over became a part of the day as well allowed-for as the Spanish siesta. Most of my friends drank too much – the more they were in tune to the times the more they drank. And so effort *per se* had no dignity against the mere bounty of those days in New York, a depreciatory word was found for it: a successful programme became a racket – I was in the literary racket.

We settled a few hours from New York and I found that every time I came to the city I was caught into a complication of events that deposited me a few days later in a somewhat exhausted state on the train for Delaware. Whole sections of the city had grown rather poisonous, but invariably I found a moment of utter peace in riding south through Central Park at dark towards where the façade of 59th Street thrusts its lights through the trees. There again was my lost city, wrapped cool in its mystery and promise. But that detachment never lasted long – as the toiler must live in the city's belly, so I was compelled to live in its disordered mind.

Instead there were the speak-easies – the moving from

luxurious bars, which advertised in the campus publications of Yale and Princeton, to the beer gardens where the snarling face of the underworld peered through the German good nature of the entertainment, then on to strange and even more sinister localities where one was eyed by granite-faced boys and there was nothing left of joviality but only a brutishness that corrupted the new day into which one presently went out. Back in 1920 I shocked a rising young business man by suggesting a cocktail before lunch. In 1929 there was liquor in half the downtown offices, and a speak-easy in half the large buildings.

One was increasingly conscious of the speak-easy and of Park Avenue. In the past decade Greenwich Village, Washington Square, Murray Hill, the chateaux of Fifth Avenue had somehow disappeared, or become unexpressive of anything. The city was bloated, gutted, stupid with cake and circuses, and a new expression 'Oh yeah?' summed up all the enthusiasm evoked by the announcement of the last super-skyscrapers. My barber retired on a half million bet in the market and I was conscious that the head waiters who bowed me, or failed to bow me, to my table were far, far wealthier than I. This was no fun – once again I had enough of New York and it was good to be safe on shipboard where the ceaseless revelry remained in the bar in transport to the fleecing rooms of France.

'What news from New York?'

'Stocks go up. A baby murdered a gangster.'

'Nothing more?'

'Nothing. Radios blare in the street.'

I once thought that there were no second acts in American lives, but there was certainly to be a second act to New York's boom days. We were somewhere in North Africa when we heard a dull distant crash which echoed to the farthest wastes of the desert.

'What was that?'

'Did you hear it?'

'It was nothing.'

'Do you think we ought to go home and see?'

'No – it was nothing.'

In the dark autumn of two years later we saw New York again. We passed through curiously polite customs agents, and then with bowed head and hat in hand I walked reverently through the echoing tomb. Among the ruins a few childish wraiths still played to keep up the pretence that they were alive, betraying by their feverish voices and hectic cheeks the thinness of the masquerade. Cocktail parties, a last hollow survival from the days of carnival, echoed to the plaints of the wounded: 'Shoot me, for the love of God, someone shoot me!', and the groans and wails of the dying: 'Did you see that United States Steel is down three more points?' My barber was back at work in his shop; again the head waiters bowed people to their tables, if there were people to be bowed. From the ruins, lonely and inexplicable as the sphinx, rose the Empire State Building and, just as it had been a tradition of mine to climb to the Plaza Roof to take leave of the beautiful city, extending as far as eyes could reach, so now I went to the roof of the last and most magnificent of towers. Then I understood – everything was explained: I had discovered the crowning error of the city, its Pandora's box. Full of vaunting pride the New Yorker had climbed here and seen with dismay what he had never suspected, that the city was not the endless succession of canyons that he had supposed but that *it had limits* – from the tallest structure he saw for the first time that it faded out into the country on all sides, into an expanse of green and blue that alone was limitless. And with the awful realization that New York was a city after all and not a universe, the whole shining edifice that he had reared in his imagination came crashing to the ground. That was the rash gift of Alfred W. Smith to the citizens of New York.

Thus I take leave of my lost city. Seen from the ferry boat in the early morning, it no longer whispers of fantastic success and eternal youth. The whoopee mamas who prance before its empty parquets do not suggest to me the ineffable beauty of my dream girls of 1914. And Bunny, swinging along confidently with his cane towards his cloister in a carnival, has gone over to Communism and frets about the wrongs of southern mill workers and western farmers whose voices, fifteen years ago, would not have penetrated his study walls.

All is lost save memory, yet sometimes I imagine myself reading, with curious interest, a *Daily News* of the issue of 1945:

MAN OF FIFTY RUNS AMUCK IN NEW YORK

Fitzgerald Feathered Many Love Nests Cutie Avers
Bumped Off By Outraged Gunman

So perhaps I am destined to return some day and find in the city new experiences that so far I have only read about. For the moment I can only cry out that I have lost my splendid mirage. Come back, come back, O glittering and white!

Ring

For a year and a half the writer of this appreciation was Ring Lardner's most familiar companion; after that, geography made separations and our contacts were rare. When my wife and I last saw him in 1931, he looked already like a man on his deathbed – it was terribly sad to see that six feet three inches of kindness stretched out ineffectual in the hospital room. His fingers trembled with a match, the tight skin on his handsome skull was marked as a mask of misery and nervous pain.

He gave a very different impression when we first saw him in 1921 – he seemed to have an abundance of quiet vitality that would enable him to outlast anyone, to take himself for long spurts of work or play that would ruin any ordinary constitution. He had recently convulsed the country with the famous kitten-and-coat saga (it had to do with a world's series bet and with the impending conversion of some kittens into fur), and the evidence of the betting, a beautiful sable, was worn by his wife at the time. In those days he was interested in people, sports, bridge, music, the stage, the newspapers, the magazines, the books. But though I did not know it, the change in him had already begun – the impenetrable despair that dogged him for a dozen years to his death.

He had practically given up sleeping, save on short vacations deliberately consecrated to simple pleasures, most frequently golf with his friends, Grantland Rice or John Wheeler. Many a night we talked over a case of Canadian ale until bright dawn, when Ring would rise and yawn:

'Well, I guess the children have left for school by this time – I might as well go home.'

The woes of many people haunted him – for example, the doctor's death sentence pronounced upon Tad, the cartoonist (who, in fact, nearly outlived Ring) – it was as if he believed he could and ought to do something about such things. And as he struggled to fulfil his contracts, one of which, a comic strip based on the character of 'the busher', was a terror, indeed, it was obvious that he felt his work to be directionless, merely 'copy'. So he was inclined to turn his cosmic sense of responsibility into the channel of solving other people's problems – finding someone an introduction to a theatrical manager, placing a friend in a job, manoeuvring a man into a good club. The effort made was often out of proportion to the situation; the truth back of it was that Ring was getting off – he was a faithful and conscientious workman to the end, but he had stopped finding any fun in his work ten years before he died.

About that time (1922) a publisher undertook to reissue his old books and collect his recent stories and this gave him a sense of existing in the literary world as well as with the public, and he got some satisfaction from the reiterated statements of Mencken and F.P.A. as to his true stature as a writer. But I don't think he cared then – it is hard to understand, but I don't think he really gave a damn about anything except his personal relations with a few people. A case in point was his attitude to those imitators who lifted everything except the shirt off his back – only Hemingway has been so thoroughly frisked – it worried the imitators more than it worried Ring. His attitude was that if they got stuck in the process he'd help them over any tough place.

Throughout this period of huge earnings and an increasingly solid reputation on top and beneath, there were two ambitions more important to Ring than the work by which he will be remembered; he wanted to be a musician – sometimes he dramatized himself ironically as a thwarted composer – and he wanted to write shows. His dealings with managers would make a whole story: they were always commissioning him to do work which they promptly forgot they had ordered, and accepting librettos that they never produced. (Ring left a short ironic record of Ziegfeld.) Only with the aid of the practical George Kaufman did he achieve his ambition, and by then he was too far gone in illness to get a proper satisfaction from it.

The point of these paragraphs is that, whatever Ring's achievement was, it fell short of the achievement he was capable of, and this because of a cynical attitude towards his work. How far back did that attitude go? – back to his youth in a Michigan village? Certainly back to his days with the Cubs. During those years, when most men of promise achieve an adult education, if only in the school of war, Ring moved in the company of a few dozen illiterates playing a boy's game. A boy's game, with no more possibilities in it than a boy could master, a game bounded by walls which kept out novelty or danger, change or adventure. This material, the observation of it under such circumstances, was the text of Ring's schooling during the most formative period of the mind. A writer can spin on about his adventures after thirty, after forty, after fifty, but the criteria by which these adventures are weighed and valued are irrevocably settled at the age of twenty-five. However deeply Ring might cut into it, his cake had exactly the diameter of Frank Chance's diamond.

Here was his artistic problem, and it promised future trouble. So long as he wrote within that enclosure the result was magnificent: within it he heard and recorded the voice of a continent. But when, inevitably, he outgrew his interest in it, what was Ring left with?

He was left with his fine linguistic technique – and he was left rather helpless in those few acres. He had been formed by the very world on which his hilarious irony had released itself. He had fought his way through to knowing what people's motives are and what means they are likely to resort to in order to attain their goals. But now he had a new problem – what to do about it. He went on seeing, and the sights travelled back to the optic nerve, but no longer to be thrown off in fiction, because they were no longer sights that could be weighed and valued by the old criteria. It was never that he was completely sold on athletic virtuosity as the be-all and end-all of problems; the trouble was that he could find nothing finer. Imagine life conceived as a business of beautiful muscular organization – an arising, an effort, a good break, a sweat, a bath, a meal, a love, a sleep – imagine it achieved; then imagine trying to apply that standard to the horribly complicated mess of living, where nothing, even the greatest conceptions and workings and achievements, is else but messy, spotty, tortuous – and then one can imagine the confusion that Ring faced on coming out of the ball park.

He kept on recording but he no longer projected, and this accumulation, which he has taken with him to the grave, crippled his spirit in the latter years. It was not the fear of Niles, Michigan, that hampered him – it was the habit of silence, formed in the presence of the 'ivory' with which he lived and worked. Remember it was not humble ivory – Ring has demonstrated that – it was arrogant, imperative, often megalomaniacal ivory. He got the habit of silence, then the habit of repression that finally took the form of his odd little crusade in the *New Yorker* against pornographic songs. He had agreed with himself to speak only a small portion of his mind.

The present writer once suggested to him that he organize some *cadre* within which he could adequately display his talents, suggesting that it should be something deeply personal, and something on which Ring could take his time, but he dismissed the idea lightly; he was a disillusioned idealist but he had served his Fates well, and no other ones could be casually created for him – 'This is something that can be printed,' he reasoned; 'this, however, belongs with that bunch of stuff that can never be written.'

He covered himself in such cases with protests of his inability to bring off anything big, but this was specious, for he was a proud man and had no reason to rate his abilities cheaply. He refused to 'tell all' because in a crucial period of his life he had formed the habit of not doing it – and this he had elevated gradually into a standard of taste. It never satisfied him by a damn sight.

So one is haunted not only by a sense of personal loss but by a conviction that Ring got less percentage of himself on paper than any other American of the first flight. There is '*You Know Me, Al*', and there are about a dozen wonderful short stories (my God, he hadn't even saved them – the material of *How to Write Short Stories* was obtained by photographing old issues in the public library!), and there is some of the most uproarious and inspired nonsense since Lewis Carroll. Most of the rest is mediocre stuff, with flashes, and I would do Ring a disservice to suggest it should be set upon an altar and worshipped, as have been the most casual relics of Mark Twain. Those three volumes should seem enough – to everyone who didn't know Ring. But I venture that no one who knew him but will agree that the personality of the man overlapped it. Proud, shy, solemn, shrewd, polite, brave, kind, merciful, honourable – with the affection these qualities aroused he created in addition a certain awe in people. His intentions, his will, once in motion, were formidable factors in dealing with him – he always did every single thing he said he would do. Frequently he was the melancholy Jaques, and sad company indeed, but under any conditions a noble dignity flowed from him, so that time in his presence always seemed well spent.

On my desk, at the moment, I have the letters Ring wrote to us; here is a letter one thousand words long, here is one of two thousand words – theatrical gossip, literary shop talk, flashes of wit but not much wit, for he was feeling thin and saving the best of that for his work, anecdotes of his activities. I reprint the most typical one I can find:

'The Dutch Treat show was a week ago Friday night. Grant Rice and I had reserved a table, and a table holds ten people and no more. Well, I had invited, as one guest, Jerry Kern, but he telephoned at the last moment that he couldn't come. I then consulted with Grant Rice, who said he had no substitute in mind, but that it was a shame to waste our extra ticket when tickets were at a premium. So I called up Jones, and Jones said yes, and would it be all right for him to bring along a former Senator who was a pal of his and had been good to him in Washington. I said I was sorry, but our table was filled and, besides, we didn't have an extra ticket. "Maybe I could dig up another ticket somewhere," said Jones. "I don't believe so," I said, "but anyway the point is that we haven't room at our table." "Well," said Jones, "I could have the Senator eat somewhere else and join us in time for the show." "Yes," I said, "but we have no ticket for him." "Well, I'll think up something," he said. Well, what he thought up was to bring himself and the Senator and I had a hell of a time getting an extra ticket and shoving the Senator in at another table where he wasn't wanted, and later in the evening, the Senator thanked Jones and said he was the greatest fella in the world and all I got was goodnight.

'Well, I must close and nibble on a carrot. R.W.L.'

Even in a telegram Ring could compress a lot of himself. Here is one: WHEN ARE YOU COMING BACK AND WHY PLEASE ANSWER RING LARDNER.

This is not the moment to recollect Ring's convivial aspects, especially as he had, long before his death, ceased to find amusement in dissipation, or indeed in the whole range of what is called entertainment – save for his perennial interest in songs. By grace of the radio and of the many musicians who, drawn by his enormous magnetism, made pilgrimages to his bedside, he had a consolation in the last days, and he made the most of it, hilariously rewriting Cole Porter's lyrics in the *New Yorker*. But it would be an evasion for the present writer not to say that when he was Ring's neighbour a decade ago, they tucked a lot under their belts in many weathers, and spent many words on many men and things. At no time did I feel that I had known him enough, or that anyone knew him – it was not the feeling that there was more stuff in him and that it should come out, it was rather a qualitative difference, it was rather as though, due to some inadequacy in one's self, one had not penetrated to something unsolved, new and unsaid. That is why one wishes that Ring had written down a large proportion of what was in his mind and heart. It would have saved him longer for us, and that in itself would be something. But I would like to know what it was, and now I will go on wishing – what did Ring want, how did he want things to be, how did he think things were?

A great and good American is dead. Let us not obscure him by the flowers, but walk up and look at that fine medallion, all abraded by sorrows that perhaps we are not equipped to understand. Ring made no enemies, because he was kind, and to many millions he gave release and delight.

The Crack-Up

February 1936

Of course all life is a process of breaking down, but the blows that do the dramatic side of the work – the big sudden blows that come, or seem to come, from outside – the ones you remember and blame things on and, in moments of weakness, tell your friends about, don't show their effect all at once. There is another sort of blow that comes from within – that you don't feel until it's too late to do anything about it, until you realize with finality that in some regard you will never be as good a man again. The first sort of breakage seems to happen quick – the second kind happens almost without your knowing it but is realized suddenly indeed.

Before I go on with this short history, let me make a general observation – the test of a first-rate intelligence is the ability to hold two opposed ideas in the mind at the same time, and still retain the ability to function. One should, for example, be able to see that things are hopeless and yet be determined to make them otherwise. This philosophy fitted on to my early adult life, when I saw the improbable, the implausible, often the 'impossible', come true. Life was something you dominated if you were any good. Life yielded easily to intelligence and effort, or to what proportion could be mustered of both. It seemed a romantic business to be a successful literary man – you were not ever going to be as famous as a movie star but what note you had was probably longer-lived – you were never going to have the power of a man of strong political or religious convictions but you were certainly more independent. Of course within the practice of your trade you were forever unsatisfied – but I, for one, would not have chosen any other.

As the twenties passed, with my own twenties marching a little ahead of them, my two juvenile regrets – at not being big enough (or good enough) to play football in college, and at not getting overseas during the war – resolved themselves into childish waking dreams of imaginary heroism that were good enough to go to sleep on in restless nights. The big problems of life seemed to solve themselves, and if the business of fixing them was difficult, it made one too tired to think of more general problems.

Life, ten years ago, was largely a personal matter. I must hold in balance the sense of the futility of effort and the sense of the necessity to struggle; the conviction of the inevitability of failure and still the determination to 'succeed' – and, more than these, the contradiction between the dead hand of the past and the high intentions of the future. If I could do this through the common ills – domestic, professional and personal – then the ego would continue as an arrow shot from nothingness to nothingness with such force that only gravity would bring it to earth at last.

For seventeen years, with a year of deliberate loafing and resting out in the centre – things went on like that, with a new chore only a nice prospect for the next day. I was living hard, too, but: 'Up to forty-nine it'll be all right,' I said. 'I can count on that. For a man who's lived as I have, that's all you could ask.'

– And then, ten years this side of forty-nine, I suddenly realized that I had prematurely cracked.

II

Now a man can crack in many ways – can crack in the head – in which case the power of decision is taken from you by others! or in the body, when one can but submit to the white hospital world; or in the nerves. William Seabrook in an unsympathetic book tells, with some pride and a movie ending, of how he became a public charge. What led to his alcoholism or was bound up with it, was a collapse of his nervous system. Though the present writer was not so entangled – having at the time not tasted so much as a glass of beer for six months – it was his nervous reflexes that were giving way – too much anger and too many tears.

Moreover, to go back to my thesis that life has a varying offensive, the realization of having cracked was not simultaneous with a blow, but with a reprieve.

Not long before, I had sat in the office of a great doctor and listened to a grave sentence. With what, in retrospect, seems some equanimity, I had gone on about my affairs in the city where I was then living, not caring much, not thinking how much had been left undone, or what would become of this and that responsibility, like people do in books; I was well insured and anyhow I had been only a mediocre caretaker of most of the things left in my hands, even of my talent.

But I had a strong sudden instinct that I must be alone. I didn't want to see any people at all. I had seen so many people all my life – I was an average mixer, but more than average in a tendency to identify myself, my ideas, my destiny, with those of all classes that I came in contact with. I was always saving or being saved – in a single morning I would go through the emotions ascribable to Wellington at Waterloo. I lived in a world of inscrutable hostiles and inalienable friends and supporters.

But now I wanted to be absolutely alone and so arranged a certain insulation from ordinary cares.

It was not an unhappy time. I went away and there were fewer people. I found I was good-and-tired. I could lie around and was glad to, sleeping or dozing sometimes twenty hours a day and in the intervals trying resolutely not to think – instead I made lists – made lists and tore them up, hundreds of lists: of cavalry leaders and football players and cities, and popular tunes and pitchers, and happy times, and hobbies and houses lived in and how many suits since I left the army and how many pairs of shoes (I didn't count the suit I bought in Sorrento that shrunk, nor the pumps and dress shirt and collar that I carried around for years and never wore, because the pumps got damp and grainy and the shirt and collar got yellow and starch-rotted). And lists of women I'd liked, and of the times I had let myself be snubbed by people who had not been my betters in character or ability.

– And then suddenly, surprisingly, I got better.

– And cracked like an old plate as soon as I heard the news.

That is the real end of this story. What was to be done about it will have to rest in what used to be called the 'womb of time'. Suffice it to say that after about an hour of solitary pillow-hugging, I began to realize that for two years my life had been a drawing on resources that I did not possess, but I had been mortgaging myself physically and spiritually up to the hilt. What was the small gift of life given back in comparison to that? – when there had once been a pride of direction and a confidence in enduring independence.

I realized that in those two years, in order to preserve something – an inner hush maybe, maybe not – I had weaned myself from all the things I used to love – that every act of life from the morning tooth-brush to the friend at dinner had become an effort. I saw that for a long time I had not liked people and things, but only followed the rickety old pretence of liking. I saw that even my love for those closest to me was become only an attempt to love, that my casual relations – with an editor, a tobacco seller, the child of a friend, were only what I remembered I *should* do, from other days. All in the same month I became bitter about such things as the sound of the radio, the advertisements in the magazines, the screech of tracks, the dead silence of the country – contemptuous at human softness, immediately (if secretively) quarrelsome towards hardness – hating the night when I couldn't sleep and hating the day because it went towards night. I slept on the heart side now because I knew that the sooner I could tire that out, even a little, the sooner would come that blessed hour of nightmare which, like a catharsis, would enable me to better meet the new day.

There were certain spots, certain faces I could look at. Like most Middle Westerners, I have never had any but the vaguest race prejudices – I always had a secret yen for the lovely Scandinavian blondes who sat on porches in St Paul but hadn't emerged enough economically to be part of what was then society. They were too nice to be 'chickens' and too quickly off the farmlands to seize a place in the sun, but I remembered going round blocks to catch a single glimpse of shining hair – the bright shock of a girl I'd never know. This is urban, unpopular talk. It strays afield from the fact that in these latter days I couldn't stand the sight of Celts, English, Politicians, Strangers, Virginians, Negroes (light or dark), Hunting People, or retail clerks, and middlemen in general, all writers (I avoided writers very carefully because they can perpetuate trouble as no one else can) – and all the classes as classes and most of them as members of their class. . . .

Trying to cling to something, I liked doctors and girl children up to the age of about thirteen and well-brought-up boy children from about eight years old on. I could have peace and happiness with these few categories of people. I forgot to add that I liked old men – men over seventy, sometimes over sixty if their faces looked seasoned. I liked Katharine Hepburn's face on the screen, no matter what was said about her pretentiousness, and Miriam Hopkins' face, and old friends if I only saw them once a year and could remember their ghosts.

All rather inhuman and undernourished, isn't it? Well, that, children, is the true sign of cracking up.

It is not a pretty picture. Inevitably it was carted here and there within its frame and exposed to various critics. One of them can only be described as a person whose life makes other people's lives seem like death – even this time when she was cast in the usually unappealing role of Job's comforter. In spite of the fact that this story is over, let me append our conversation as a sort of postscript:

'Instead of being so sorry for yourself, listen –' she said. (She always says 'Listen', because she thinks while she talks – *really* thinks.) So she said: 'Listen. Suppose this wasn't a crack in you – suppose it was a crack in the Grand Canyon.'

'The crack's in me,' I said heroically.

'Listen! The world only exists in your eyes – your conception of it. You can make it as big or as small as you want to. And you're trying to be a little puny individual. By God, if I ever cracked, I'd try to make the world crack with me. Listen! The world only exists through your apprehension of it, and so it's much better to say that it's not you that's cracked – it's the Grand Canyon.'

'Baby et up all her Spinoza?'

'I don't know anything about Spinoza. I know –' She spoke, then, of old woes of her own, that seemed, in the telling, to have been more dolorous than mine, and how she had met them, over-ridden them, beaten them.

I felt a certain reaction to what she said, but I am a slow-thinking man, and it occurred to me simultaneously that of all natural forces, vitality is the incommunicable one. In days when juice came into one as an article without duty, one tried to distribute it – but always without success; to further mix metaphors, vitality never 'takes'. You have it or you haven't it, like health or brown eyes or honour or a baritone voice. I might have asked some of it from her, neatly wrapped and ready for home cooking and digestion, but I could never have got it – not if I'd waited around for a thousand hours with the tin cup of self-pity. I could walk from her door, holding myself very carefully like cracked crockery, and go away into the world of bitterness, where I was making a home with such materials as are found there – and quote to myself after I left her door:

'Ye are the salt of the earth. But if the salt hath lost its savour, wherewith shall it be salted?'

Matthew 5–13.

HANDLE WITH CARE *March 1936*

In a previous article this writer told about his realization that what he had before him was not the dish that he had ordered for his forties. In fact – since he and the dish were one, he described himself as a cracked plate, the kind that one wonders whether it is worth preserving. Your editor thought that the article suggested too many aspects without regarding them closely, and probably many readers felt the same way – and there are always those to whom all self-revelation is contemptible, unless it ends with a noble thanks to the gods for the Unconquerable Soul.

But I had been thanking the gods too long, and thanking them for nothing. I wanted to put a lament into my record, without even the background of the Euganean Hills to give it colour. There weren't any Euganean hills that I could see.

Sometimes, though, the cracked plate has to be retained in the pantry, has to be kept in service as a household necessity. It can never again be warmed on the stove nor shuffled with the other plates in the dishpan; it will not be brought out for company, but it will do to hold crackers late at night or to go into the ice box under left-overs. . . .

Hence this sequel – a cracked plate's further history.

Now the standard cure for one who is sunk is to consider those in actual destitution or physical suffering – this is an all-weather beatitude for gloom in general and fairly salutary day-time advice for everyone. But at three o'clock in the morning, a forgotten package has the same tragic importance as a death sentence, and the cure doesn't work – and in a real dark night of the soul it is always three o'clock in the morning, day after day. At that hour the tendency is to refuse to face things as long as possible by retiring into an infantile dream – but one is continually startled out of this by various contacts with the world. One meets these occasions as quickly and carelessly as possible and retires once more back into the dream, hoping that things will adjust themselves by some great material or spiritual bonanza. But as the withdrawal persists there is less and less chance of the bonanza – one is not waiting for the fade-out of a single sorrow, but rather being an unwilling witness of an execution, the disintegration of one's own personality....

Unless madness or drugs or drink come into it, this phase comes to a dead-end, eventually, and is succeeded by a vacuous quiet. In this you can try to estimate what has been sheared away and what is left. Only when this quiet came to me, did I realize that I had gone through two parallel experiences.

The first time was twenty years ago, when I left Princeton in junior year with a complaint diagnosed as malaria. It transpired, through an X-ray taken a dozen years later, that it had been tuberculosis – a mild case, and after a few months of rest I went back to college. But I had lost certain offices, the chief one was the presidency of the Triangle Club, a musical comedy idea, and also I dropped back a class. To me college would never be the same. There were to be no badges of pride, no medals, after all. It seemed on one March afternoon that I had lost every single thing I wanted – and that night was the first time that I hunted down the spectre of womanhood that, for a little while, makes everything else seem unimportant.

Years later I realized that my failure as a big shot in college was all right – instead of serving on committees, I took a beating on English poetry; when I got the idea of what it was all about, I set about learning how to write. On Shaw's principle that 'If you don't get what you like, you better like what you get', it was a lucky break – at the moment it was a harsh and bitter business to know that my career as a leader of men was over.

Since that day I have not been able to fire a bad servant, and I am astonished and impressed by people who can. Some old desire for personal dominance was broken and gone. Life around me was a solemn dream, and I lived on the letters I wrote to a girl in another city. A man does not recover from such jolts – he becomes a different person and, eventually, the new person finds new things to care about.

The other episode parallel to my current situation took place after the war, when I had again over-extended my flank. It was one of those tragic loves doomed for lack of money, and one day the girl closed it out on the basis of common sense. During a long summer of despair I wrote a novel instead of letters, so it came out all right, but it came out all right for a different person. The man with the jingle of money in his pocket who married the girl a year later would always cherish an abiding distrust, an animosity, towards the leisure class – not the conviction of a revolutionist but the smouldering hatred of a peasant. In the years since then I have never been able to stop wondering where my friends' money came from, nor to stop thinking that at one time a sort of *droit de seigneur* might have been exercised to give one of them my girl.

For sixteen years I lived pretty much as this latter person, distrusting the rich, yet working for money with which to share their mobility and the grace that some of them brought into their lives. During this time I had plenty of the usual horses shot from under me – I remember some of their names – *Punctured Pride*, *Thwarted Expectation*, *Faithless*, *Show-off*, *Hard Hit*, *Never Again*. And after a while I wasn't twenty-five, then not even thirty-five, and nothing was quite as good. But in all these years I don't remember a moment of discouragement. I saw honest men through moods of suicidal gloom – some of them gave up and died; others adjusted themselves and went on to a larger success than mine; but my morale never sank below the level of self-disgust when I had put on some unsightly personal show. Trouble has no necessary connexion with discouragement – discouragement has a germ of its own, as different from trouble as arthritis is different from a stiff joint.

When a new sky cut off the sun last spring, I didn't at first relate it to what had happened fifteen or twenty years ago. Only gradually did a certain family resemblance come through – an over-extension of the flank, a burning of the candle at both ends; a call upon physical resources that I did not command, like a man over-drawing at his bank. In its impact this blow was more violent than the other two but it was the same in kind – a feeling that I was standing at twilight on a deserted range, with an empty rifle in my hands and the targets down. No problem set – simply a silence with only the sound of my own breathing.

In this silence there was a vast irresponsibility towards every obligation, a deflation of all my values. A passionate belief in order, a disregard of motives or consequences in favour of guess work and prophecy, a feeling that craft and industry would have a place in any world – one by one, these and other convictions were swept away. I saw that the novel, which at my maturity was the strongest and supplest medium for conveying thought and emotion from one human being to another, was becoming subordinated to a mechanical and communal art that, whether in the hands of Hollywood merchants or Russian idealists, was capable of reflecting only the tritest thought, the most obvious emotion. It was an art in which words were subordinate to images, where personality was worn down to the inevitable low gear of collaboration. As long past as 1930, I had a hunch that the talkies would make even the best selling novelist as archaic as silent pictures. People still read, if only Professor Canby's book of the month – curious children nosed at the slime of Mr Tiffany Thayer in the drug-store libraries – but there was a rankling indignity, that to me had become almost an obsession, in seeing the power of the written word subordinate to another power, a more glittering, a grosser power....

I set that down as an example of what haunted me during the long night – this was something I could neither accept nor struggle against, something which tended to make my efforts obsolescent, as the chain stores have crippled the small merchant, an exterior force, unbeatable –

(I have the sense of lecturing now, looking at a watch on the desk before me and seeing how many more minutes –)

Well, when I had reached this period of silence, I was forced into a measure that no one ever adopts voluntarily: I was impelled to think. God, was it difficult! The moving about of great secret trunks. In the first exhausted halt, I wondered whether I had ever thought. After a long time I came to these conclusions, just as I write them here:

(1) That I had done very little thinking, save within the problems of my craft. For twenty years a certain man had been my intellectual conscience. That was Edmund Wilson.

(2) That another man represented my sense of the 'good life', though I saw him once in a decade, and since then he

might have been hung. He is in the fur business in the Northwest and wouldn't like his name set down here. But in difficult situations I had tried to think what *he* would have thought, how *he* would have acted.

(3) That a third contemporary had been an artistic conscience to me – I had not imitated his infectious style, because my own style, such as it is, was formed before he published anything, but there was an awful pull towards him when I was on a spot.

(4) That a fourth man had come to dictate my relations with other people when these relations were successful: how to do, what to say. How to make people at least momentarily happy (in opposition to Mrs Post's theories of how to make everyone thoroughly uncomfortable with a sort of systematized vulgarity). This always confused me and made me want to go out and get drunk, but this man had seen the game, analysed it and beaten it, and his word was good enough for me.

(5) That my political conscience had scarcely existed for ten years save as an element of irony in my stuff. When I became again concerned with the system I should function under, it was a man much younger than myself who brought it to me, with a mixture of passion and fresh air.

So there was not an 'I' any more – not a basis on which I could organize my self-respect – save my limitless capacity for toil that it seemed I possessed no more. It was strange to have no self – to be like a little boy left alone in a big house, who knew that now he could do anything he wanted to do, but found that there was nothing that he wanted to do –

(The watch is past the hour and I have barely reached my thesis. I have some doubts as to whether this is of general interest, but if anyone wants more, there is plenty left, and your editor will tell me. If you've had enough, say so – but not too loud, because I have the feeling that someone, I'm not sure who, is sound asleep – someone who could have helped me to keep my shop open. It wasn't Lenin, and it wasn't God.)

PASTING IT TOGETHER

April 1936

I have spoken in these pages of how an exceptionally optimistic young man experienced a crack-up of all values, a crack-up that he scarcely knew of until long after it occurred. I told of the succeeding period of desolation and of the necessity of going on, but without benefit of Henley's familiar heroics, 'my head is bloody but unbowed.' For a check-up of my spiritual liabilities indicated that I had no particular head to be bowed or unbowed. Once I had a heart but that was about all I was sure of.

This was at least a starting place out of the morass in which I floundered: 'I felt – therefore I was.' At one time or another there had been many people who had leaned on me, come to me in difficulties or written me from afar, believed implicitly in my advice and my attitude towards life. The dullest platitude monger or the most unscrupulous Rasputin who can influence the destinies of many people must have some individuality, so the question became one of finding why and where I had changed, where was the leak through which, unknown to myself, my enthusiasm and my vitality had been steadily and prematurely trickling away.

One harassed and despairing night I packed a brief-case and went off a thousand miles to think it over. I took a dollar room in a drab little town where I knew no one and sunk all the money I had with me in a stock of potted meat, crackers, and apples. But don't let me suggest that the change from a rather overstuffed world to a comparative asceticism was any Research Magnificent – I only wanted absolute quiet to think out why I had developed a sad attitude towards sadness, a melancholy attitude towards melancholy, and a tragic attitude towards tragedy – *why I had become identified with the objects of my horror or compassion.*

Does this seem a fine distinction? It isn't: identification such as this spells the death of accomplishment. It is something like this that keeps insane people from working. Lenin did not willingly endure the sufferings of his proletariat, nor Washington of his troops, nor Dickens of his London poor. And when Tolstoy tried some such merging of himself with the objects of his attention, it was a fake and a failure. I mention these because they are the men best known to us all.

It was dangerous mist. When Wordsworth decided that 'there had passed away a glory from the earth', he felt no compulsion to pass away with it, and the Fiery Particle Keats never ceased his struggle against t.b. nor in his last moments relinquished his hope of being among the English poets.

My self-immolation was something sodden-dark. It was very distinctly not modern – yet I saw it in others, saw it in a dozen men of honour and industry since the war. (I heard you, but that's too easy – there were Marxians among these men.) I had stood by while one famous contemporary of mine played with the idea of the Big Out for half a year; I had watched when another, equally eminent, spent months in an asylum unable to endure any contact with his fellow men. And of those who had given up and passed on I could list a score.

This led me to the idea that the ones who had survived had made some sort of clean break. This is a big word and is no parallel to a jail-break when one is probably headed for a new jail or will be forced back to the old one. The famous 'Escape' or 'run away from it all' is an excursion in a trap even if the trap includes the south seas, which are only for those who want to paint them or sail them. A clean break is something you cannot come back from; that is irretrievable because it makes the past cease to exist. So, since I could no longer fulfil the obligations that life had set for me or that I had set for myself, why not slay the empty shell who had been posturing at it for four years? I must continue to be a writer because that was my only way of life, but I would cease any attempts to be a person – to be kind, just, or generous. There were plenty of counterfeit coins around that would pass instead of these and I knew where I could get them at a nickel on the dollar. In thirty-nine years an observant eye has learned to detect where the milk is watered and the sugar is sanded, the rhinestone passed for diamond and the stucco for stone. There was to be no more giving of myself – all giving was to be outlawed henceforth under a new name, and that name was Waste.

The decision made me rather exuberant, like anything that is both real and new. As a sort of beginning there was a whole shaft of letters to be tipped into the waste basket when I went home, letters that wanted something for nothing – to read this man's manuscript, market this man's poem, speak free on the radio, indite notes of introduction, give this interview, help with the plot of this play, with this domestic situation, perform this act of thoughtfulness or charity.

The conjuror's hat was empty. To draw things out of it had long been a sort of sleight of hand, and now, to change the metaphor, I was off the dispensing end of the relief roll forever.

The heady villainous feeling continued.

I felt like the beady-eyed men I used to see on the commuting train from Great Neck fifteen years back – men who didn't care whether the world tumbled into chaos tomorrow if it spared their houses. I was one with them now, one with the smooth articles who said:

'I'm sorry but business is business.' Or:

'You ought to have thought of that before you got into this trouble.' Or:

'I'm not the person to see about that.'

And a smile – ah, I would get me a smile. I'm still working on that smile. It is to combine the best qualities of an hotel manager, an experienced old social weasel, a headmaster on visitors' day, a coloured elevator man, a pansy pulling a profile, a producer getting stuff at half its market value, a trained nurse coming on a new job, a body-vender in her first rotogravure, a hopeful extra swept near the camera, a ballet dancer with an infected toe, and of course the great beam of loving kindness common to all those from Washington to Beverly Hills who must exist by virtue of the contorted pan.

The voice too – I am working with a teacher on the voice. When I have perfected it the larynx will show no ring of conviction except the conviction of the person I am talking to. Since it will be largely called upon for the elicitation of the word 'Yes', my teacher (a lawyer) and I are concentrating on that, but in extra hours. I am learning to bring into it that polite acerbity that makes people feel that far from being welcome they are not even tolerated and are under continual and scathing analysis at every moment. These times will of course not coincide with the smile. This will be reserved exclusively for those from whom I have nothing to gain, old worn-out people or young struggling people. They won't mind – what the hell, they get it most of the time anyhow.

But enough. It is not a matter of levity. If you are young and you should write asking to see me and learn how to be a sombre literary man writing pieces upon the state of emotional exhaustion that often overtakes writers in their prime – if you should be so young and so fatuous as to do this, I would not do so much as acknowledge your letter, unless you were related to someone very rich and important indeed. And if you were dying of starvation outside my window, I would go out quickly and give you the smile and the voice (if no longer the hand) and stick around till somebody raised a nickel to phone for the ambulance, that is if I thought there would be any copy in it for me.

I have now at last become a writer only. The man I had persistently tried to be became such a burden that I have 'cut him loose' with as little compunction as a Negro lady cuts loose a rival on Saturday night. Let the good people function as such – let the overworked doctors die in harness, with one week's 'vacation' a year that they can devote to straightening out their family affairs, and let the underworked doctors scramble for cases at one dollar a throw; let the soldiers be killed and enter immediately into the Valhalla of their profession. That is their contract with the gods. A writer need have no such ideals unless he makes them for himself, and this one has quit. The old dream of being an entire man in the Goethe-Byron-Shaw tradition, with an opulent American touch, a sort of combination of J. P. Morgan, Topham Beauclerk and St Francis of Assisi, has been relegated to the junk heap of the shoulder pads worn for one day on the Princeton freshman football field and the overseas cap never worn overseas.

So what? This is what I think now: that the natural state of the sentient adult is a qualified unhappiness. I think also that in an adult the desire to be finer in grain than you are, 'a constant striving' (as those people say who gain their bread by saying it) only adds to this unhappiness in the end – that end that comes to our youth and hope. My own happiness in the past often approached such an ecstasy that I could not share it even with the person dearest to me but had to walk it away in quiet streets and lanes with only fragments of it to distil into little lines in books – and I think that my happiness, or talent for self-delusion or what you will, was an exception. It was not the natural thing but the unnatural – unnatural as the Boom; and my recent experience parallels the wave of despair that swept the nation when the Boom was over.

I shall manage to live with the new dispensation, though it has taken some months to be certain of the fact. And just as the laughing stoicism which has enabled the American Negro to endure the intolerable conditions of his existence has cost him his sense of the truth – so in my case there is a price to pay. I do not any longer like the postman, nor the grocer, nor the editor, nor the cousin's husband, and he in turn will come to dislike me, so that life will never be very pleasant again, and the sign *Cave Canem* is hung permanently just above my door. I will try to be a correct animal though, and if you throw me a bone with enough meat on it I may even lick your hand.

Early Success

Seventeen years ago this month I quit work or, if you prefer, I retired from business. I was through – let the Street Railway Advertising Company carry along under its own power. I retired, not on my profit, but on my liabilities, which included debts, despair, and a broken engagement, and crept home to St Paul to 'finish a novel'.

That novel, begun in a training camp late in the war, was my ace in the hole. I had put it aside when I got a job in New York, but I was as constantly aware of it as of the shoe with cardboard in the sole, during all one desolate spring. It was like the fox and goose and the bag of beans. If I stopped working to finish the novel, I lost the girl.

So I struggled on in a business I detested and all the confidence I had garnered at Princeton and in a haughty career as an army's worst aide-de-camp melted gradually away. Lost and forgotten, I walked quickly from certain places – from the pawnshop where one left the field-glasses, from prosperous friends whom one met when wearing the suit from before the war – from restaurants after tipping with the last nickel, from busy cheerful offices that were saving the jobs for their own boys from the war.

Even having a first story accepted had not proved very exciting. Dutch Mount and I sat across from each other in a car-card slogan advertising office, and the same mail brought each of us an acceptance from the same magazine – the old *Smart Set*.

'My cheque was thirty – how much was yours?'

'Thirty-five.'

The real blight, however, was that my story had been written in college two years before, and a dozen new ones hadn't even drawn a personal letter. The implication was that I was on the down-grade at twenty-two. I spent the thirty dollars on a magenta feather fan for a girl in Alabama.

My friends who were not in love, or who had waiting arrangements with 'sensible' girls, braced themselves patiently for a long pull. Not I – I was in love with a whirlwind and I must spin a net big enough to catch it out of my head, a head full of trickling nickels and sliding dimes, the incessant music box of the poor. It couldn't be done like that, so when the girl threw me over I went home and finished my novel. And then, suddenly, everything changed, and this article is about that first wild wind of success and the delicious mist it brings with it. It is a short and precious time – for when the mist rises in a few weeks, or a few months, one finds that the very best is over.

It began to happen in the autumn of 1919 when I was an empty bucket, so mentally blunted with the summer's writing that I'd taken a job repairing car roofs at the Northern Pacific shops. Then the postman rang, and that day I quit work and ran along the street, stopping automobiles to tell friends and acquaintances about it – my novel *This Side of Paradise* was accepted for publication. That week the postman rang and rang, and I paid off my terrible small debts, bought a suit, and woke up every morning with a world of ineffable toploftiness and promise.

While I waited for the novel to appear, the metamorphosis of amateur into professional began to take place – a sort of stitching together of your whole life into a pattern of work, so that the end of one job is automatically the beginning of another. I had been an amateur before; in October, when I strolled with a girl among the stones of a southern graveyard, I was a professional and my enchantment with certain things that she felt and said was already paced by an anxiety to set them down in a story – it was called *The Ice Palace* and it was published later. Similarly, during Christmas week in St Paul, there was a night when I had stayed home from two dances to work on a story. Three friends called up during the evening to tell me I had missed some rare doings: a well-known man-about-town had disguised himself as a camel and, with a taxi-driver as the rear half, managed to attend the wrong party. Aghast with myself for not being there, I spent the next day trying to collect the fragments of the story.

'Well, all I can say is it was funny when it happened.' 'No, I don't know where he got the taxi-man.' 'You'd have to know him well to understand how funny it was.'

In despair I said:

'Well, I can't seem to find out exactly what happened but I'm going to write about it as if it was ten times funnier than anything you've said.' So I wrote it, in twenty-two consecutive hours, and wrote it 'funny', simply because I was so emphatically told it was funny. *The Camel's Back* was published and still crops up in the humorous anthologies.

With the end of the winter set in another pleasant pumped-dry period, and, while I took a little time off, a fresh picture of life in America began to form before my eyes. The uncertainties of 1919 were over – there seemed little doubt about what was going to happen – America was going on the greatest, gaudiest spree in history and there was going to be plenty to tell about it. The whole golden boom was in the air – its splendid generosities, its outrageous corruptions and the tortuous death struggle of the old America in prohibition. All the stories that came into my head had a touch of disaster in them – the lovely young creatures in my novels went to ruin, the diamond mountains of my short stories blew up, my millionaires were as beautiful and damned as Thomas Hardy's peasants. In life these things hadn't happened yet, but I was pretty sure living wasn't the reckless, careless business these people thought – this generation just younger than me.

For my point of vantage was the dividing line between the two generations, and there I sat – somewhat self-consciously. When my first big mail came in – hundreds and hundreds of letters on a story about a girl who bobbed her hair – it seemed rather absurd that they should come to me about it. On the other hand, for a shy man it was nice to be somebody except oneself again: to be 'the Author' as one had been 'the Lieutenant'. Of course one wasn't really an author any more than one had been an army officer, but nobody seemed to guess behind the false face.

All in three days I got married and the presses were pounding out *This Side of Paradise* like they pound out extras in the movies.

With its publication I had reached a stage of manic-depressive insanity. Rage and bliss alternated hour by hour. A lot of people thought it was a fake, and perhaps it was, and a lot of others thought it was a lie, which it was not. In a daze I gave out an interview – I told what a great writer I was and how I'd achieved the heights. Heywood Broun, who was on my trail, simply quoted it with the comment that I seemed to be a very self-satisfied young man, and for some days I was notably poor company. I invited him to lunch and in a kindly way told him that it was too bad he had let his life slide away without accomplishing anything. He had just turned thirty and it was about then that I wrote a line which certain people will not let me forget: 'She was a faded but still lovely woman of twenty-seven.'

In a daze I told the Scribner Company that I didn't expect my novel to sell more than twenty thousand copies and when the laughter died away I was told that a sale of five thousand was excellent for a first novel. I think it was a week after publication that it passed the twenty thousand mark, but I took myself so seriously that I didn't even think it was funny.

These weeks in the clouds ended abruptly a week later when Princeton turned on the book – not undergraduate Princeton but the black mass of faculty and alumni. There was a kind but reproachful letter from President Hibben, and a room full of classmates who suddenly turned on me with condemnation. We had been part of a rather gay party staged conspicuously in Harvey Firestone's car of robin's-egg blue, and in the course of it I got an accidental black eye trying to stop a fight. This was magnified into an orgy, and in spite of a delegation of undergraduates who went to the board of Governors, I was suspended from my club for a couple of months. The *Alumni Weekly* got after my book and only Dean Gauss had a good word to say for me. The unctuousness and hypocrisy of the proceedings was exasperating and for seven years I didn't go to Princeton. Then a magazine asked me for an article about it, and when I started to write it, I found I really loved the place and that the experience of one week was a small item in the total budget. But on that day in 1920 most of the joy went out of my success.

But one was now a professional – and the new world couldn't possibly be presented without bumping the old out of the way. One gradually developed a protective hardness against both praise and blame. Too often people liked your things for the wrong reasons or people liked them whose dislike would be a compliment. No decent career was ever founded on a public and one learned to go ahead without precedents and without fear. Counting the bag, I found that in 1919 I had made $800 by writing, that in 1920 I had made $18,000, stories, picture rights, and book. My story price had gone from $30 to $1,000. That's a small price to what was paid later in the Boom, but what it sounded like to me couldn't be exaggerated.

The dream had been early realized and the realization carried with it a certain bonus and a certain burden. Premature success gives one an almost mystical conception of destiny as opposed to will-power – at its worst the Napoleonic delusion. The man who arrives young believes that he exercises his will because his star is shining. The man who only asserts himself at thirty has a balanced idea of what will-power and fate have each contributed, the one who gets there at forty is liable to put the emphasis on will alone. This comes out when the storms strike your craft.

The compensation of a very early success is a conviction that life is a romantic matter. In the best sense one stays young. When the primary objects of love and money could be taken for granted and a shaky eminence had lost its fascination, I had fair years to waste, years that I can't honestly regret, in seeking the eternal Carnival by the Sea. Once in the middle twenties I was driving along the High Corniche Road through the twilight with the whole French Riviera twinkling on the sea below. As far ahead as I could see was Monte Carlo, and though it was out of season and there were no Grand Dukes left to gamble and E. Phillips Oppenheim was a fat industrious man in my hotel, who lived in a bath-robe – the very name was so incorrigibly enchanting that I could only stop the car and like the Chinese whisper: 'Ah me! Ah me!' It was not Monte Carlo I was looking at. It was back into the mind of the young man with cardboard soles who had walked the streets of New York. I was him again – for an instant I had the good fortune to share his dreams, I who had no more dreams of my own. And there are still times when I creep up on him, surprise him on an autumn morning in New York or a spring night in Carolina when it is so quiet that you can hear a dog barking in the next county. But never again as during that all too short period when he and I were one person, when the fulfilled future and the wistful past were mingled in a single gorgeous moment – when life was literally a dream.

Stories

Gretchen's Forty Winks

The sidewalks were scratched with brittle leaves, and the bad little boy next door froze his tongue to the iron mail-box. Snow before night, sure. Autumn was over. This, of course, raised the coal question and the Christmas question; but Roger Halsey, standing on his own front porch, assured the dead suburban sky that he hadn't time for worrying about the weather. Then he let himself hurriedly into the house, and shut the subject out into the cold twilight.

The hall was dark, but from above he heard the voices of his wife and the nursemaid and the baby in one of their interminable conversations, which consisted chiefly of 'Don't!' and 'Look out, Maxy!' and 'Oh, there he *goes*!' punctuated by wild threats and vague bumpings and the recurrent sound of small, venturing feet.

Roger turned on the hall-light and walked into the living-room and turned on the red silk lamp. He put his bulging portfolio on the table, and sitting down rested his intense young face in his hand for a few minutes, shading his eyes carefully from the light. Then he lit a cigarette, squashed it out, and going to the foot of the stairs called for his wife.

'Gretchen!'

'Hello, dear.' Her voice was full of laughter. 'Come see baby.'

He swore softly.

'I can't see baby now,' he said aloud. 'How long 'fore you'll be down?'

There was a mysterious pause, and then a succession of

'Don'ts' and 'Look outs, Maxy' evidently meant to avert some threatened catastrophe.

'How long 'fore you'll be down?' repeated Roger, slightly irritated.

'Oh, I'll be right down.'

'How soon?' he shouted.

He had trouble every day at this hour in adapting his voice from the urgent key of the city to the proper casualness for a model home. But tonight he was deliberately impatient. It almost disappointed him when Gretchen came running down the stairs, three at a time, crying 'What is it?' in a rather surprised voice.

They kissed – lingered over it some moments. They had been married three years, and they were much more in love than that implies. It was seldom that they hated each other with that violent hate of which only young couples are capable, for Roger was still actively sensitive to her beauty.

'Come in here,' he said abruptly. 'I want to talk to you.'

His wife, a bright-coloured, Titian-haired girl, vivid as a French rag doll, followed him into the living room.

'Listen, Gretchen' – he sat down at the end of the sofa – 'beginning with tonight I'm going to – What's the matter?'

'Nothing. I'm just looking for a cigarette. Go on.'

She tiptoed breathlessly back to the sofa and settled at the other end.

'Gretchen –' Again he broke off. Her hand, palm upward, was extended towards him. 'Well, what is it?' he asked wildly.

'Matches.'

'What?'

In his impatience it seemed incredible that she should ask for matches, but he fumbled automatically in his pocket.

'Thank you,' she whispered. 'I didn't mean to interrupt you. Go on.'

'Gretch —'

Scratch! The match flared. They exchanged a tense look. Her fawn's eyes apologized mutely this time, and he laughed. After all, she had done no more than light a cigarette; but when he was in this mood her slightest positive action irritated him beyond measure.

'When you've got time to listen,' he said crossly, 'you might be interested in discussing the poorhouse question with me.'

'What poorhouse?' Her eyes were wide, startled; she sat quiet as a mouse.

'That was just to get your attention. But, beginning tonight, I start on what'll probably be the most important six weeks of my life – the six weeks that'll decide whether we're going on forever in this rotten little house in this rotten little suburban town.'

Boredom replaced alarm in Gretchen's black eyes. She was a Southern girl, and any question that had to do with getting ahead in the world always tended to give her a headache.

'Six months ago I left the New York Lithographic Company,' announced Roger, 'and went in the advertising business for myself.'

'I know,' interrupted Gretchen resentfully; 'and now instead of getting six hundred a month sure, we're living on a risky five hundred.'

'Gretchen,' said Roger sharply, 'if you'll just believe in me as hard as you can for six weeks more we'll be rich. I've got a chance now to get some of the biggest accounts in the country.' He hesitated. 'And for these six weeks we won't go out at all, and we won't have anyone here. I'm going to bring home work every night, and we'll pull down all the blinds and if anyone rings the doorbell we won't answer.'

He smiled airily as if it were a new game they were going to play. Then, as Gretchen was silent, his smile faded, and he looked at her uncertainly.

'Well, what's the matter?' she broke out finally. 'Do you expect me to jump up and sing? You do enough work as it is. If you try to do any more you'll end up with a nervous breakdown. I read about a –'

'Don't worry about me,' he interrupted; 'I'm all right. But you're going to be bored to death sitting here every evening.'

'No, I won't,' she said without conviction – 'except tonight.'

'What about tonight?'

'George Tompkins asked us to dinner.'

'Did you accept?'

'Of course I did,' she said impatiently. 'Why not? You're always talking about what a terrible neighbourhood this is, and I thought maybe you'd like to go to a nicer one for a change.'

'When I go to a nicer neighbourhood I want to go for good,' he said grimly.

'Well, can we go?'

'I suppose we'll have to if you've accepted.'

Somewhat to his annoyance the conversation abruptly ended. Gretchen jumped up and kissed him sketchily and rushed into the kitchen to light the hot water for a bath. With a sigh he carefully deposited his portfolio behind the bookcase – it contained only sketches and layouts for display advertising, but it seemed to him the first thing a burglar would look for. Then he went abstractedly upstairs, dropping into the baby's room for a casual moist kiss, and began dressing for dinner.

They had no automobile, so George Tompkins called for them at 6.30. Tompkins was a successful interior decorator, a broad, rosy man with a handsome moustache and a strong odour of jasmine. He and Roger had once roomed side by side in a boarding-house in New York, but they had met only intermittently in the past five years.

'We ought to see each other more,' he told Roger tonight. 'You ought to go out more often, old boy. Cocktail?'

'No, thanks.'

'No? Well, your fair wife will – won't you, Gretchen?'

'I love this house,' she exclaimed, taking the glass and looking admiringly at ship models, Colonial whisky bottles, and other fashionable débris of 1925.

'I like it,' said Tompkins with satisfaction. 'I did it to please myself, and I succeeded.'

Roger stared moodily around the stiff, plain room, wondering if they could have blundered into the kitchen by mistake.

'You look like the devil, Roger,' said his host. 'Have a cocktail and cheer up.'

'Have one,' urged Gretchen.

'What?' Roger turned around absently. 'Oh, no, thanks. I've got to work after I get home.'

'Work!' Tompkins smiled. 'Listen, Roger, you'll kill yourself with work. Why don't you bring a little balance into your life – work a little, then play a little?'

'That's what I tell him,' said Gretchen.

'Do you know an average business man's day?' demanded Tompkins as they went in to dinner. 'Coffee in the morning, eight hours' work interrupted by a bolted luncheon, and then home again with dyspepsia and a bad temper to give the wife a pleasant evening.'

Roger laughed shortly.

'You've been going to the movies too much,' he said dryly.

'What?' Tompkins looked at him with some irritation. 'Movies? I've hardly ever been to the movies in my life. I think the movies are atrocious. My opinions on life are drawn from my own observations. I believe in a balanced life.'

'What's that?' demanded Roger.

'Well' – he hesitated – 'probably the best way to tell you

would be to describe my own day. Would that seem horribly egotistic?'

'Oh, no!' Gretchen looked at him with interest. 'I'd love to hear about it.'

'Well, in the morning I get up and go through a series of exercises. I've got one room fitted up as a little gymnasium, and I punch the bag and do shadow-boxing and weight-pulling for an hour. Then after a cold bath – There's a thing now! Do you take a daily cold bath?'

'No,' admitted Roger, 'I take a hot bath in the evening three or four times a week.'

A horrified silence fell. Tompkins and Gretchen exchanged a glance as if something obscene had been said.

'What's the matter?' broke out Roger, glancing from one to the other in some irritation. 'You know I don't take a bath every day – I haven't got the time.'

Tompkins gave a prolonged sigh.

'After my bath,' he continued, drawing a merciful veil of silence over the matter, 'I have breakfast and drive to my office in New York, where I work until four. Then I lay off, and if it's summer I hurry out here for nine holes of golf, or if it's winter I play squash for an hour at my club. Then a good snappy game of bridge until dinner. Dinner is liable to have something to do with business, but in a pleasant way. Perhaps I've just finished a house for some customer, and he wants me to be on hand for his first party to see that the lighting is soft enough and all that sort of thing. Or maybe I sit down with a good book of poetry and spend the evening alone. At any rate, I do something every night to get me out of myself.'

'It must be wonderful,' said Gretchen enthusiastically. 'I wish we lived like that.'

Tompkins bent forward earnestly over the table.

'You can,' he said impressively. 'There's no reason why

you shouldn't. Look here, if Roger'll play nine holes of golf every day it'll do wonders for him. He won't know himself. He'll do his work better, never get that tired, nervous feeling – What's the matter?'

He broke off. Roger had perceptibly yawned.

'Roger,' cried Gretchen sharply, 'there's no need to be so rude. If you did what George said, you'd be a lot better off.' She turned indignantly to their host. 'The latest is that he's going to work at night for the next six weeks. He says he's going to pull down the blinds and shut us up like hermits in a cave. He's been doing it every Sunday for the last year; now he's going to do it every night for six weeks.'

Tompkins shook his head sadly.

'At the end of six weeks,' he remarked, 'he'll be starting for the sanatorium. Let me tell you, every private hospital in New York is full of cases like yours. You just strain the human nervous system a little too far, and bang! – you've broken something. And in order to save sixty hours you're laid up sixty weeks for repairs.' He broke off, changed his tone, and turned to Gretchen with a smile. 'Not to mention what happens to you. It seems to me it's the wife rather than the husband who bears the brunt of these insane periods of overwork.'

'I don't mind,' protested Gretchen loyally.

'Yes, she does,' said Roger grimly; 'she minds like the devil. She's a shortsighted little egg, and she thinks it's going to be forever until I get started and she can have some new clothes. But it can't be helped. The saddest thing about women is that, after all, their best trick is to sit down and fold their hands.'

'Your ideas on women are about twenty years out of date,' said Tompkins pityingly. 'Women won't sit down and wait any more.'

'Then they'd better marry men of forty,' insisted Roger stubbornly. 'If a girl marries a young man for love she ought to be willing to make any sacrifice within reason, so long as her husband keeps going ahead.'

'Let's not talk about it,' said Gretchen impatiently. 'Please, Roger, let's have a good time just this once.'

When Tompkins dropped them in front of their house at eleven Roger and Gretchen stood for a moment on the sidewalk looking at the winter moon. There was a fine, damp, dusty snow in the air, and Roger drew a long breath of it and put his arm around Gretchen exultantly.

'I can make more money than he can,' he said tensely. 'And I'll be doing it in just forty days.'

'Forty days,' she sighed. 'It seems such a long time – when everybody else is always having fun. If I could only sleep for forty days.'

'Why don't you, honey? Just take forty winks, and when you wake up everything'll be fine.'

She was silent for a moment.

'Roger,' she asked thoughtfully, 'do you think George meant what he said about taking me horseback riding on Sunday?'

Roger frowned.

'I don't know. Probably not – I hope to Heaven he didn't.' He hesitated. 'As a matter of fact, he made me sort of sore tonight – all that junk about his cold bath.'

With their arms about each other, they started up the walk to the house.

'I'll bet he doesn't take a cold bath every morning,' continued Roger ruminatively; 'or three times a week, either.' He fumbled in his pocket for the key and inserted it in the lock with savage precision. Then he turned around defiantly. 'I'll bet he hasn't had a bath for a month.'

II

After a fortnight of intensive work, Roger Halsey's days blurred into each other and passed by in blocks of twos and threes and fours. From eight until 5.30 he was in his office. Then a half-hour on the commuting train, where he scrawled notes on the backs of envelopes under the dull yellow light. By 7.30 his crayons, shears, and sheets of white cardboard were spread over the living-room table, and he laboured there with much grunting and sighing until midnight, while Gretchen lay on the sofa with a book, and the doorbell tinkled occasionally behind the drawn blinds. At twelve there was always an argument as to whether he would come to bed. He would agree to come after he had cleared up everything; but as he was invariably sidetracked by half a dozen new ideas, he usually found Gretchen sound asleep when he tiptoed upstairs.

Sometimes it was three o'clock before Roger squashed his last cigarette into the overloaded ash-tray, and he would undress in the dark, disembodied with fatigue, but with a sense of triumph that he had lasted out another day.

Christmas came and went and he scarcely noticed that it was gone. He remembered it afterwards as the day he completed the window-cards for Garrod's shoes. This was one of the eight large accounts for which he was pointing in January – if he got half of them he was assured a quarter of a million dollars' worth of business during the year.

But the world outside his business became a chaotic dream. He was aware that on two cool December Sundays George Tompkins had taken Gretchen horseback riding, and that another time she had gone out with him in his automobile to spend the afternoon skiing on the country-club hill. A picture of Tompkins, in an expensive frame, had appeared one morning on their bedroom wall. And one night he was shocked into a startled protest when Gretchen went to the theatre with Tompkins in town.

But his work was almost done. Daily now his layouts arrived from the printers until seven of them were piled and docketed in his office safe. He knew how good they were. Money alone couldn't buy such work; more than he realized himself, it had been a labour of love.

December tumbled like a dead leaf from the calendar. There was an agonizing week when he had to give up coffee because it made his heart pound so. If he could hold on now for four days – three days –

On Thursday afternoon H. G. Garrod was to arrive in New York. On Wednesday evening Roger came home at seven to find Gretchen poring over the December bills with a strange expression in her eyes.

'What's the matter?'

She nodded at the bills. He ran through them, his brow wrinkling in a frown.

'Gosh!'

'I can't help it,' she burst out suddenly. 'They're terrible.'

'Well, I didn't marry you because you were a wonderful housekeeper. I'll manage about the bills some way. Don't worry your little head over it.'

She regarded him coldly.

'You talk as if I were a child.'

'I have to,' he said with sudden irritation.

'Well, at least I'm not a piece of bric-à-brac that you can just put somewhere and forget.'

He knelt down by her quickly, and took her arms in his hands.

'Gretchen, listen!' he said breathlessly. 'For God's sake, don't go to pieces now! We're both all stored up with malice and reproach, and if we had a quarrel it'd be terrible. I love you, Gretchen. Say you love me – quick!'

'You know I love you.'

The quarrel was averted, but there was an unnatural tenseness all through dinner. It came to a climax afterwards when he began to spread his working materials on the table.

'Oh, Roger,' she protested, 'I thought you didn't have to work tonight.'

'I didn't think I'd have to, but something came up.'

'I've invited George Tompkins over.'

'Oh, gosh!' he exclaimed. 'Well, I'm sorry, honey, but you'll have to phone him not to come.'

'He's left,' she said. 'He's coming straight from town. He'll be here any minute now.'

Roger groaned. It occurred to him to send them both to the movies, but somehow the suggestion stuck on his lips. He did not want her at the movies; he wanted her here, where he could look up and know she was by his side.

George Tompkins arrived breezily at eight o'clock. 'Aha!' he cried reprovingly, coming into the room. 'Still at it.'

Roger agreed coolly that he was.

'Better quit – better quit before you have to.' He sat down with a long sigh of physical comfort and lit a cigarette. 'Take it from a fellow who's looked into the question scientifically. We can stand so much, and then – bang!'

'If you'll excuse me' – Roger made his voice as polite as possible – 'I'm going upstairs and finish this work.'

'Just as you like, Roger.' George waved his hand carelessly. 'It isn't that I mind. I'm the friend of the family and I'd just as soon see the missus as the mister.' He smiled playfully. 'But if I were you, old boy, I'd put away my work and get a good night's sleep.'

When Roger had spread out his materials on the bed upstairs he found that he could still hear the rumble and murmur of their voices through the thin floor. He began wondering what they found to talk about. As he plunged deeper into his work his mind had a tendency to revert sharply to his question, and several times he arose and paced nervously up and down the room.

The bed was ill adapted to his work. Several times the paper slipped from the board on which it rested, and the pencil punched through. Everything was wrong tonight. Letters and figures blurred before his eyes, and as an accompaniment to the beating of his temples came those persistent murmuring voices.

At ten he realized that he had done nothing for more than an hour, and with a sudden exclamation he gathered together his papers, replaced them in his portfolio, and went downstairs. They were sitting together on the sofa when he came in.

'Oh, hello!' cried Gretchen, rather unnecessarily, he thought. 'We were just discussing you.'

'Thank you,' he answered ironically. 'What particular part of my anatomy was under the scalpel?'

'Your health,' said Tompkins jovially.

'My health's all right,' answered Roger shortly.

'But you look at it so selfishly, old fella,' cried Tompkins. 'You only consider yourself in the matter. Don't you think Gretchen has any rights? If you were working on a wonderful sonnet or a – a portrait of some madonna or something' – he glanced at Gretchen's Titian hair – 'why, then I'd say go ahead. But you're not. It's just some silly advertisement about how to sell Nobald's hair tonic, and if all the hair tonic ever made was dumped into the ocean tomorrow the world wouldn't be one bit the worse for it.'

'Wait a minute,' said Roger angrily; 'that's not quite fair. I'm not kidding myself about the importance of my work – it's just as useless as the stuff you do. But to Gretchen and me it's just about the most important thing in the world.'

'Are you implying that my work is useless?' demanded Tompkins incredulously.

'No; not if it brings happiness to some poor sucker of a pants manufacturer who doesn't know how to spend his money.'

Tompkins and Gretchen exchanged a glance.

'Oh-h-h!' exclaimed Tompkins ironically. 'I didn't realize that all these years I've just been wasting my time.'

'You're a loafer,' said Roger rudely.

'Me?' cried Tompkins angrily. 'You call me a loafer because I have a little balance in my life and find time to do interesting things? Because I play hard as well as work hard and don't let myself get to be a dull, tiresome drudge?'

Both men were angry now, and their voices had risen, though on Tompkins' face there still remained the semblance of a smile.

'What I object to,' said Roger steadily, 'is that for the last six weeks you seem to have done all your playing around here.'

'Roger!' cried Gretchen. 'What do you mean by talking like that?'

'Just what I said.'

'You've just lost your temper.' Tompkins lit a cigarette with ostentatious coolness. 'You're so nervous from overwork you don't know what you're saying. You're on the verge of a nervous break –'

'You get out of here!' cried Roger fiercely. 'You get out of here right now – before I throw you out!'

Tompkins got angrily to his feet.

'You – you throw me out?' he cried incredulously.

They were actually moving towards each other when Gretchen stepped between them, and grabbing Tompkins' arm urged him towards the door.

'He's acting like a fool, George, but you better get out,' she cried, groping in the hall for his hat.

'He insulted me!' shouted Tompkins. 'He threatened to throw me out!'

'Never mind, George,' pleaded Gretchen. 'He doesn't know what he's saying. Please go! I'll see you at ten o'clock tomorrow.'

She opened the door.

'You won't see him at ten o'clock tomorrow,' said Roger steadily. 'He's not coming to this house any more.'

Tompkins turned to Gretchen.

'It's his house,' he suggested. 'Perhaps we'd better meet at mine.'

Then he was gone, and Gretchen had shut the door behind him. Her eyes were full of angry tears.

'See what you've done!' she sobbed. 'The only friend I had, the only person in the world who liked me enough to treat me decently, is insulted by my husband in my own house.'

She threw herself on the sofa and began to cry passionately into the pillows.

'He brought it on himself,' said Roger stubbornly. 'I've stood as much as my self-respect will allow. I don't want you going out with him any more.'

'I will go out with him!' cried Gretchen wildly. 'I'll go out with him all I want! Do you think it's any fun living here with you?'

'Gretchen,' he said coldly, 'get up and put on your hat and coat and go out that door and never come back!'

Her mouth fell slightly ajar.

'But I don't want to get out,' she said dazedly.

'Well, then, behave yourself.' And he added in a gentler voice: 'I thought you were going to sleep for this forty days.'

'Oh, yes,' she cried bitterly, 'easy enough to say! But I'm tired of sleeping.' She got up, faced him defiantly. 'And what's more, I'm going riding with George Tompkins tomorrow.'

'You won't go out with him if I have to take you to New York and sit you down in my office until I get through.'

She looked at him with rage in her eyes.

'I hate you,' she said slowly. 'And I'd like to take all the work you've done and tear it up and throw it in the fire. And just to give you something to worry about tomorrow, I probably won't be here when you get back.'

She got up from the sofa, and very deliberately looked at her flushed, tear-stained face in the mirror. Then she ran upstairs and slammed herself into the bedroom.

Automatically Roger spread out his work on the living-room table. The bright colours of the designs, the vivid ladies – Gretchen had posed for one of them – holding orange ginger ale or glistening silk hosiery, dazzled his mind into a sort of coma. His restless crayon moved here and there over the pictures, shifting a block of letters half an inch to the right, trying a dozen blues for a cool blue, and eliminating the word that made a phrase anaemic and pale. Half an hour passed – he was deep in the work now; there was no sound in the room but the velvety scratch of the crayon over the glossy board.

After a long while he looked at his watch – it was after three. The wind had come up outside and was rushing by the house corners in loud, alarming swoops, like a heavy body falling through space. He stopped his work and listened. He was not tired now, but his head felt as if it was covered with bulging veins like those pictures that hang in doctors' offices showing a body stripped of decent skin. He put his hands to his head and felt it all over. It seemed to him that on his temple the veins were knotty and brittle around an old scar.

Suddenly he began to be afraid. A hundred warnings he had heard swept into his mind. People did wreck themselves with overwork, and his body and brain were of the same vulnerable and perishable stuff. For the first time he found himself envying George Tompkins' calm nerves and healthy routine. He arose and began pacing the room in a panic.

'I've got to sleep,' he whispered to himself tensely. 'Otherwise I'm going crazy.'

He rubbed his hand over his eyes, and returned to the

table to put up his work, but his fingers were shaking so that he could scarcely grasp the board. The sway of a bare branch against the window made him start and cry out. He sat down on the sofa and tried to think.

'Stop! Stop! Stop!' the clock said. 'Stop! Stop! Stop!'

'I can't stop,' he answered aloud. 'I can't afford to stop.'

Listen! Why, there was the wolf at the door now! He could hear its sharp claws scrape along the varnished woodwork. He jumped up, and running to the front door flung it open; then started back with a ghastly cry. An enormous wolf was standing on the porch, glaring at him with red, malignant eyes. As he watched it the hair bristled on its neck; it gave a low growl and disappeared in the darkness. Then Roger realized with a silent, mirthless laugh that it was the police dog from over the way.

Dragging his limbs wearily into the kitchen, he brought the alarm-clock into the living-room and set it for seven. Then he wrapped himself in his overcoat, lay down on the sofa and fell immediately into a heavy, dreamless sleep.

When he awoke the light was still shining feebly, but the room was the grey colour of a winter morning. He got up, and looking anxiously at his hands found to his relief that they no longer trembled. He felt much better. Then he began to remember in detail the events of the night before, and his brow drew up again in three shallow wrinkles. There was work ahead of him, twenty-four hours of work; and Gretchen, whether she wanted to or not, must sleep for one more day.

Roger's mind glowed suddenly as if he had just thought of a new advertising idea. A few minutes later he was hurrying through the sharp morning air to Kingsley's drug-store.

'Is Mr Kingsley down yet?'

The druggist's head appeared around the corner of the prescription-room.

'I wonder if I can talk to you alone.'

At 7.30, back home again, Roger walked into his own kitchen. The general housework girl had just arrived and was taking off her hat.

'Bebé' – he was not on familiar terms with her; this was her name – 'I want you to cook Mrs Halsey's breakfast right away. I'll take it up myself.'

It struck Bebé that this was an unusual service for so busy a man to render his wife, but if she had seen his conduct when he had carried the tray from the kitchen she would have been even more surprised. For he set it down on the dining room table and put into the coffee half a teaspoonful of a white substance that was not powdered sugar. Then he mounted the stairs and opened the door of the bedroom.

Gretchen woke up with a start, glanced at the twin bed which had not been slept in, and bent on Roger a glance of astonishment, which changed to contempt when she saw the breakfast in his hand. She thought he was bringing it as a capitulation.

'I don't want any breakfast,' she said coldly, and his heart sank, 'except some coffee.'

'No breakfast?' Roger's voice expressed disappointment.

'I said I'd take some coffee.'

Roger discreetly deposited the tray on a table beside the bed and returned quickly to the kitchen.

'We're going away until tomorrow afternoon,' he told Bebé, 'and I want to close up the house right now. So you just put on your hat and go home.'

He looked at his watch. It was ten minutes to eight, and he wanted to catch the 8.10 train. He waited five minutes and then tiptoed softly upstairs and into Gretchen's room. She was sound asleep. The coffee cup was empty save for black dregs and a film of thin brown paste on the bottom. He looked at her rather anxiously, but her breathing was regular and clear.

From the closet he took a suitcase and very quickly began

filling it with her shoes – street shoes, evening slippers, rubber-soled oxfords – he had not realized that she owned so many pairs. When he closed the suitcase it was bulging.

He hesitated a minute, took a pair of sewing scissors from a box, and following the telephone-wire until it went out of sight behind the dresser, severed it in one neat clip. He jumped as there was a soft knock at the door. It was the nursemaid. He had forgotten her existence.

'Mrs Halsey and I are going up to the city till tomorrow,' he said glibly. 'Take Maxy to the beach and have lunch there. Stay all day.'

Back in the room, a wave of pity passed over him. Gretchen seemed suddenly lovely and helpless, sleeping there. It was somehow terrible to rob her young life of a day. He touched her hair with his fingers, and as she murmured something in her dream he leaned over and kissed her bright cheek. Then he picked up the suitcase full of shoes, locked the door, and ran briskly down the stairs.

III

By five o'clock that afternoon the last package of cards for Garrod's shoes had been sent by messenger to H. G. Garrod at the Biltmore Hotel. He was to give a decision next morning. At 5.30 Roger's stenographer tapped him on the shoulder.

'Mr Golden, the superintendent of the building, to see you.'

Roger turned around dazedly.

'Oh, how do?'

Mr Golden came directly to the point. If Mr Halsey intended to keep the office any longer, the little oversight about the rent had better be remedied right away.

'Mr Golden,' said Roger wearily, 'everything'll be all right tomorrow. If you worry me now maybe you'll never get your money. After tomorrow nothing'll matter.'

Mr Golden looked at the tenant uneasily. Young men sometimes did away with themselves when business went wrong. Then his eye fell unpleasantly on the initialled suitcase beside the desk.

'Going on a trip?' he asked pointedly.

'What? Oh, no. That's just some clothes.'

'Clothes, eh? Well, Mr Halsey, just to prove that you mean what you say, suppose you let me keep that suitcase until tomorrow noon.'

'Help yourself.'

Mr Golden picked it up with a deprecatory gesture.

'Just a matter of form,' he remarked.

'I understand,' said Roger, swinging around to his desk. 'Good afternoon.'

Mr Golden seemed to feel that the conversation should close on a softer key.

'And don't work too hard, Mr Halsey. You don't want to have a nervous break –'

'No,' shouted Roger, 'I don't. But I will if you don't leave me alone.'

As the door closed behind Mr Golden, Roger's stenographer turned sympathetically around.

'You shouldn't have let him get away with that,' she said. 'What's in there? Clothes?'

'No,' answered Roger absently. 'Just all my wife's shoes.'

He slept in the office that night on a sofa beside his desk. At dawn he awoke with a nervous start, rushed out into the street for coffee, and returned in ten minutes in a panic – afraid that he might have missed Mr Garrod's telephone call. It was then 6.30.

By eight o'clock his whole body seemed to be on fire. When his two artists arrived he was stretched on the couch in almost physical pain. The phone rang imperatively at 9.30, and he picked up the receiver with trembling hands.

'Hello.'

'Is this the Halsey agency?'

'Yes, this is Mr Halsey speaking.'

'This is Mr H. G. Garrod.'

Roger's heart stopped beating.

'I called up, young fellow, to say that this is wonderful work you've given us here. We want all of it and as much more as your office can do.'

'Oh, God!' cried Roger into the transmitter.

'What?' Mr H. G. Garrod was considerably startled. 'Say, wait a minute there!'

But he was talking to nobody. The phone had clattered to the floor, and Roger, stretched full length on the couch, was sobbing as if his heart would break.

IV

Three hours later, his face somewhat pale, but his eyes calm as a child's, Roger opened the door of his wife's bedroom with the morning paper under his arm. At the sound of his footsteps she started awake.

'What time is it?' she demanded.

He looked at his watch.

'Twelve o'clock.'

Suddenly she began to cry.

'Roger,' she said brokenly, 'I'm sorry I was so bad last night.'

He nodded coolly.

'Everything's all right now,' he answered. Then, after a pause: 'I've got the account – the biggest one.'

She turned towards him quickly.

'You have?' Then, after a minute's silence: 'Can I get a new dress?'

'Dress?' He laughed shortly. 'You can get a dozen. This account alone will bring us in forty thousand a year. It's one of the biggest in the West.'

She looked at him, startled.

'Forty thousand a year!'

'Yes.'

'Gosh' – and then faintly – 'I didn't know it'd really be anything like that.' Again she thought a minute. 'We can have a house like George Tompkins'.'

'I don't want an interior-decoration shop.'

'Forty thousand a year!' she repeated again, and then added softly: 'Oh, Roger –'

'Yes?'

'I'm not going out with George Tompkins.'

'I wouldn't let you, even if you wanted to,' he said shortly.

She made a show of indignation.

'Why, I've had a date with him for this Thursday for weeks.'

'It isn't Thursday.'

'It is.'

'It's Friday.'

'Why, Roger, you must be crazy! Don't you think I know what day it is?'

'It isn't Thursday,' he said stubbornly. 'Look!' And he held out the morning paper.

'Friday!' she exclaimed. 'Why, this is a mistake! This must be last week's paper. Today's Thursday.'

She closed her eyes and thought for a moment.

'Yesterday was Wednesday,' she said decisively. 'The laundress came yesterday. I guess I know.'

'Well,' he said smugly, 'look at the paper. There isn't any question about it.'

With a bewildered look on her face she got out of bed and began searching for her clothes. Roger went into the bathroom to shave. A minute later he heard the springs creak again. Gretchen was getting back into bed.

'What's the matter?' he inquired, putting his head around the corner of the bathroom.

'I'm scared,' she said in a trembling voice. 'I think my nerves are giving way. I can't find any of my shoes.'

'Your shoes? Why, the closet's full of them.'

'I know, but I can't see one.' Her face was pale with fear. 'Oh, Roger!'

Roger came to her bedside and put his arm around her.

'Oh, Roger,' she cried, 'what's the matter with me? First that newspaper, and now all my shoes. Take care of me, Roger.'

'I'll get the doctor,' he said.

He walked remorselessly to the telephone and took up the receiver.

'Phone seems to be out of order,' he remarked after a minute; 'I'll send Bebé.'

The doctor arrived in ten minutes.

'I think I'm on the verge of a collapse,' Gretchen told him in a strained voice.

Doctor Gregory sat down on the edge of the bed and took her wrist in his hand.

'It seems to be in the air this morning.'

'I got up,' said Gretchen in an awed voice, 'and I found that I'd lost a whole day. I had an engagement to go riding with George Tompkins –'

'What?' exclaimed the doctor in surprise. Then he laughed.

'George Tompkins won't go riding with anyone for many days to come.'

'Has he gone away?' asked Gretchen curiously.

'He's going West.'

'Why?' demanded Roger. 'Is he running away with somebody's wife?'

'No,' said Doctor Gregory. 'He's had a nervous breakdown.'

'What?' they exclaimed in unison.

'He just collapsed like an opera-hat in his cold shower.'

'But he was always talking about his – his balanced life,' gasped Gretchen. 'He had it on his mind.'

'I know,' said the doctor. 'He's been babbling about it all morning. I think it's driven him a little mad. He worked pretty hard at it, you know.'

'At what?' demanded Roger in bewilderment.

'At keeping his life balanced.' He turned to Gretchen. 'Now all I'll prescribe for this lady here is a good rest. If she'll just stay around the house for a few days and take forty winks of sleep she'll be as fit as ever. She's been under some strain.'

'Doctor,' exclaimed Roger hoarsely, 'don't you think I'd better have a rest or something? I've been working pretty hard lately.'

'You!' Doctor Gregory laughed, slapped him violently on the back. 'My boy, I never saw you looking better in your life.'

Roger turned away quickly to conceal his smile – winked forty times, or almost forty times, at the autographed picture of Mr George Tompkins, which hung slightly askew on the bedroom wall.

The Last of the Belles

I

After Atlanta's elaborate and theatrical rendition of Southern charm, we all underestimated Tarleton. It was a little hotter than anywhere we'd been – a dozen rookies collapsed the first day in that Georgia sun – and when you saw herds of cows drifting through the business streets, hi-yaed by coloured drovers, a trance stole down over you out of the hot light: you wanted to move a hand or foot to be sure you were alive.

So I stayed out at camp and let Lieutenant Warren tell me about the girls. This was fifteen years ago, and I've forgotten how I felt, except that the days went along, one after another, better than they do now, and I was empty-hearted, because up North she whose legend I had loved for three years was getting married. I saw the clippings and newspaper photographs. It was 'a romantic wartime wedding', all very rich and sad. I felt vividly the dark radiance of the sky under which it took place and, as a young snob, was more envious than sorry.

A day came when I went into Tarleton for a haircut and ran into a nice fellow named Bill Knowles, who was in my time at Harvard. He'd been in the National Guard division that preceded us in camp; at the last moment he had transferred to aviation and had been left behind.

'I'm glad I met you, Andy,' he said with undue seriousness. 'I'll hand you on all my information before I start for Texas. You see, there're really only three girls here –'

I was interested; there was something mystical about there being three girls.

'– and here's one of them now.'

We were in front of a drug store and he marched me in and introduced me to a lady I promptly detested.

'The other two are Ailie Calhoun and Sally Carrol Happer.'

I guessed from the way he pronounced her name that he was interested in Ailie Calhoun. It was on his mind what she would be doing while he was gone; he wanted her to have a quiet, uninteresting time.

At my age I don't even hesitate to confess that entirely unchivalrous images of Ailie Calhoun – that lovely name – rushed into my mind. At twenty-three there is no such thing as a pre-empted beauty; though, had Bill asked me, I would doubtless have sworn in all sincerity to care for her like a sister. He didn't; he was just fretting out loud at having to go. Three days later he telephoned me that he was leaving next morning and he'd take me to her house that night.

We met at the hotel and walked uptown through the flowery, hot twilight. The four white pillars of the Calhoun house faced the street, and behind them the veranda was dark as a cave with hanging, weaving, climbing vines.

When we came up the walk a girl in a white dress tumbled out of the front door, crying, 'I'm so sorry I'm late!' and seeing us, added: 'Why, I thought I heard you come ten minutes –'

She broke off as a chair creaked and another man, an aviator from Camp Harry Lee, emerged from the obscurity of the veranda.

'Why, Canby!' she cried. 'How are you?'

He and Bill Knowles waited with the tenseness of open litigants.

'Canby, I want to whisper to you, honey,' she said, after just a second. 'You'll excuse us, Bill.'

They went aside. Presently Lieutenant Canby, immensely displeased, said in a grim voice, 'Then we'll make it Thursday, but that means sure.' Scarcely nodding to us, he went down the walk, the spurs with which he presumably urged on his aeroplane gleaming in the lamplight.

'Come in – I don't just know your name –'

There she was – the Southern type in all its purity. I would have recognized Ailie Calhoun if I'd never heard Ruth Draper or read Marse Chan. She had the adroitness sugar-coated with sweet, voluble simplicity, the suggested background of devoted fathers, brothers and admirers stretching back into the South's heroic age, the unfailing coolness acquired in the endless struggle with the heat. There were notes in her voice that ordered slaves around, that withered up Yankee captains, and then soft, wheedling notes that mingled in unfamiliar loveliness with the night.

I could scarcely see her in the darkness, but when I rose to go – it was plain that I was not to linger – she stood in the orange light from the doorway. She was small and very blonde; there was too much fever-coloured rouge on her face, accentuated by a nose dabbed clownish white, but she shone through that like a star.

'After Bill goes I'll be sitting here all alone night after night. Maybe you'll take me to the country-club dances.' The pathetic prophecy brought a laugh from Bill. 'Wait a minute,' Ailie murmured. 'Your guns are all crooked.'

She straightened my collar pin, looking up at me for a second with something more than curiosity. It was a seeking look, as if she asked, 'Could it be you?' Like Lieutenant Canby, I marched off unwillingly into the suddenly insufficient night.

Two weeks later I sat with her on the same veranda, or rather she half lay in my arms, and yet scarcely touched me

– how she managed that I don't remember. I was trying unsuccessfully to kiss her, and had been trying for the best part of an hour. We had a sort of joke about my not being sincere. My theory was that if she'd let me kiss her I'd fall in love with her. Her argument was that I was obviously insincere.

In a lull between two of these struggles she told me about her brother who had died in his senior year at Yale. She showed me his picture – it was a handsome, earnest face with a Leyendecker forelock – and told me that when she met someone who measured up to him she'd marry. I found this family idealism discouraging; even my brash confidence couldn't compete with the dead.

The evening and other evenings passed like that, and ended with my going back to camp with the remembered smell of magnolia flowers and a mood of vague dissatisfaction. I never kissed her. We went to the vaudeville and to the country club on Saturday nights, where she seldom took ten consecutive steps with one man, and she took me to barbecues and rowdy watermelon parties, and never thought it was worth while to change what I felt for her into love. I see now that it wouldn't have been hard, but she was a wise nineteen and she must have seen that we were emotionally incompatible. So I became her confidant instead.

We talked about Bill Knowles. She was considering Bill; for, though she wouldn't admit it, a winter at school in New York and a prom at Yale had turned her eyes North. She said she didn't think she'd marry a Southern man. And by degrees I saw that she was consciously and voluntarily different from these other girls who sang nigger songs and shot craps in the country-club bar. That's why Bill and I and others were drawn to her. We recognized her.

June and July, while the rumours reached us faintly, ineffectually, of battle and terror overseas, Ailie's eyes roved here and there about the country-club floor, seeking for something among the tall young officers. She attached several, choosing them with unfailing perspicacity – save in the case of Lieutenant Canby, whom she claimed to despise, but, nevertheless, gave dates to 'because he was so sincere' – and we apportioned her evenings among us all summer.

One day she broke all her dates – Bill Knowles had leave and was coming. We talked of the event with scientific impersonality – would he move her to a decision? Lieutenant Canby, on the contrary, wasn't impersonal at all; made a nuisance of himself. He told her that if she married Knowles he was going to climb up six thousand feet in his aeroplane, shut off the motor and let go. He frightened her – I had to yield him my last date before Bill came.

On Saturday night she and Bill Knowles came to the country club. They were very handsome together and once more I felt envious and sad. As they danced out on the floor the three-piece orchestra was playing *After You've Gone*, in a poignant incomplete way that I can hear yet, as if each bar were trickling off a precious minute of that time. I knew then that I had grown to love Tarleton, and I glanced about half in panic to see if some face wouldn't come in for me out of that warm, singing, outer darkness that yielded up couple after couple in organdie and olive drab. It was a time of youth and war, and there was never so much love around.

When I danced with Ailie she suddenly suggested that we go outside to a car. She wanted to know why didn't people cut in on her tonight? Did they think she was already married?

'Are you going to be?'

'I don't know, Andy. Sometimes, when he treats me as if I were sacred, it thrills me.' Her voice was hushed and far away. 'And then –'

She laughed. Her body, so frail and tender, was touching

mine, her face was turned up to me, and there, suddenly, with Bill Knowles ten yards off, I could have kissed her at last. Our lips just touched experimentally; then an aviation officer turned a corner of the veranda near us, peered into our darkness, and hesitated.

'Ailie.'

'Yes.'

'You heard about this afternoon?'

'What?' She leaned forward, tenseness already in her voice.

'Horace Canby crashed. He was instantly killed.'

She got up slowly and stepped out of the car.

'You mean he was killed?' she said.

'Yes. They don't know what the trouble was. His motor –'

'Oh-h-h!' Her rasping whisper came through the hands suddenly covering her face. We watched her helplessly as she put her head on the side of the car, gagging dry tears. After a minute I went for Bill, who was standing in the stag line, searching anxiously about for her, and told him she wanted to go home.

I sat on the steps outside. I had disliked Canby, but his terrible, pointless death was more real to me then than the day's toll of thousands in France. In a few minutes Ailie and Bill came out. Ailie was whimpering a little, but when she saw me her eyes flexed and she came over swiftly.

'Andy' – she spoke in a quick, low voice – 'of course you must never tell anybody what I told you about Canby yesterday. What he said, I mean.'

'Of course not.'

She looked at me a second longer as if to be quite sure. Finally she was sure. Then she sighed in such a quaint little way that I could hardly believe my ears, and her brow went up in what can only be described as mock despair.

'An-dy!'

I looked uncomfortably at the ground, aware that she

was calling my attention to her involuntarily disastrous effect on men.

'Good night, Andy!' called Bill as they got into a taxi.

'Good night,' I said, and almost added: 'You poor fool.'

II

Of course I should have made one of those fine moral decisions that people make in books, and despised her. On the contrary, I don't doubt that she could still have had me by raising her hand.

A few days later she made it all right by saying wistfully, 'I know you think it was terrible of me to think of myself at a time like that, but it was such a shocking coincidence.'

At twenty-three I was entirely unconvinced about anything, except that some people were strong and attractive and could do what they wanted, and others were caught and disgraced. I hoped I was of the former. I was sure Ailie was.

I had to revise other ideas about her. In the course of a long discussion with some girl about kissing – in those days people still talked about kissing more than they kissed – I mentioned the fact that Ailie had only kissed two or three men, and only when she thought she was in love. To my considerable disconcertion the girl figuratively just lay on the floor and howled.

'But it is true,' I assured her, suddenly knowing it wasn't. 'She told me herself.'

'Ailie Calhoun! Oh, my heavens! Why, last year at the Tech spring house party –'

This was in September. We were going overseas any week now, and to bring us up to full strength a last batch of officers from the fourth training camp arrived. The fourth camp wasn't like the first three – the candidates were from the ranks; even from the drafted divisions. They had queer names without vowels in them, and save for a few young militiamen, you couldn't take it for granted that they came out of any background at all. The addition to our company was Lieutenant Earl Schoen from New Bedford, Massachusetts; as fine a physical specimen as I have ever seen. He was six-foot-three, with black hair, high colour, and glossy dark-brown eyes. He wasn't very smart and he was definitely illiterate, yet he was a good officer, high-tempered and commanding, and with that becoming touch of vanity that sits well on the military. I had an idea that New Bedford was a country town, and set down his bumptious qualities to that.

We were doubled up in living quarters and he came into my hut. Inside of a week there was a cabinet photograph of some Tarleton girl nailed brutally to the shack wall.

'She's no jane or anything like that. She's a society girl; goes with all the best people here.'

The following Sunday afternoon I met the lady at a semi-private swimming pool in the country. When Ailie and I arrived, there was Schoen's muscular body rippling out of a bathing suit at the far end of the pool.

'Hey, lieutenant!'

When I waved back at him he grinned and winked, jerking his head towards the girl at his side. Then, digging her in the ribs, he jerked his head at me. It was a form of introduction.

'Who's that with Kitty Preston?' Ailie asked, and when I told her she said he looked like a street-car conductor, and pretended to look for her transfer.

A moment later he crawled powerfully and gracefully down the pool and pulled himself up at our side. I introduced him to Ailie.

'How do you like my girl, lieutenant?' he demanded. 'I told you she was all right, didn't I?' He jerked his head towards Ailie; this time to indicate that his girl and Ailie moved in the same circles. 'How about us all having dinner together down at the hotel some night?'

I left them in a moment, amused as I saw Ailie visibly making up her mind that here, anyhow, was not the ideal. But Lieutenant Earl Schoen was not to be dismissed so lightly. He ran his eyes cheerfully and inoffensively over her cute, slight figure, and decided that she would do even better than the other. Then minutes later I saw them in the water together, Ailie swimming away with a grim little stroke she had, and Schoen wallowing riotously around her and ahead of her, sometimes pausing and staring at her, fascinated, as a boy might look at a nautical doll.

While the afternoon passed he remained at her side. Finally Ailie came over to me and whispered, with a laugh: 'He's afollowing me around. He thinks I haven't paid my car-fare.'

She turned quickly. Miss Kitty Preston, her face curiously flustered, stood facing us.

'Ailie Calhoun, I didn't think it of you to go out and delib'ately try to take a man away from another girl.' – An expression of distress at the impending scene flitted over Ailie's face – 'I thought you considered yourself above anything like that.'

Miss Preston's voice was low, but it held that tensity that can be felt farther than it can be heard, and I saw Ailie's clear lovely eyes glance about in panic. Luckily, Earl himself was ambling cheerfully and innocently towards us.

'If you care for him you certainly oughtn't to belittle yourself in front of him,' said Ailie in a flash, her head high.

It was her acquaintance with the traditional way of behaving against Kitty Preston's naïve and fierce possessiveness, or if you prefer it, Ailie's 'breeding' against the other's 'commonness'. She turned away.

'Wait a minute kid!' cried Earl Schoen. 'How about your address? Maybe I'd like to give you a ring on the phone.'

She looked at him in a way that should have indicated to Kitty her entire lack of interest.

'I'm very busy at the Red Cross this month,' she said, her voice as cool as her slicked-back blonde hair. 'Goodbye.'

On the way home she laughed. Her air of having been unwittingly involved in a contemptible business vanished.

'She'll never hold that young man,' she said. 'He wants somebody new.'

'Apparently he wants Ailie Calhoun.'

The idea amused her.

'He could give me his ticket punch to wear, like a fraternity pin. What fun! If Mother ever saw anybody like that come in the house, she'd just lie down and die.'

And to give Ailie credit, it was fully a fortnight before he did come to her house, although he rushed her until she pretended to be annoyed at the next country-club dance.

'He's the biggest tough, Andy,' she whispered to me. 'But he's so sincere.'

She used the word 'tough' without the conviction it would have carried had he been a Southern boy. She only knew it with her mind; her ear couldn't distinguish between one Yankee voice and another. And somehow Mrs Calhoun didn't expire at his appearance on the threshold. The supposedly ineradicable prejudices of Ailie's parents were a convenient phenomenon that disappeared at her wish. It was her friends who were astonished. Ailie, always a little above Tarleton, whose beaux had been very carefully the 'nicest' men of the camp – Ailie and Lieutenant Schoen! I grew tired of assuring people that she was merely distracting herself – and indeed every week or so there was someone new – an ensign from Pensacola, an old friend from New Orleans – but always, in between times, there was Earl Schoen.

Orders arrived for an advance party of officers and sergeants to proceed to the port of embarkation and take ship to France. My name was on the list. I had been on the range for a week and when I got back to camp, Earl Schoen buttonholed me immediately.

'We're giving a little farewell party in the mess. Just you and I and Captain Craker and three girls.'

Earl and I were to call for the girls. We picked up Sally Carrol Happer and Nancy Lamar, and went on to Ailie's house; to be met at the door by the butler with the announcement that she wasn't home.

'Isn't home?' Earl repeated blankly. 'Where is she?'

'Didn't leave no information about that; just said she wasn't home.'

'But this is a darn funny thing!' he exclaimed. He walked around the familiar dusky veranda while the butler waited at the door. Something occurred to him. 'Say,' he informed me – 'say, I think she's sore.'

I waited. He said sternly to the butler, 'You tell her I've got to speak to her a minute.'

'How'm I goin' tell her that when she ain't home?'

Again Earl walked musingly around the porch. Then he nodded several times and said:

'She's sore at something that happened downtown.'

In a few words he sketched out the matter to me.

'Look here; you wait in the car,' I said. 'Maybe I can fix this.' And when he reluctantly retreated: 'Oliver, you tell Miss Ailie I want to see her alone.'

After some argument he bore this message and in a moment returned with a reply:

'Miss Ailie say she don't want to see that other gentleman about nothing never. She say come in if you like.'

She was in the library. I had expected to see a picture of cool, outraged dignity, but her face was distraught, tumultuous, despairing. Her eyes were red-rimmed, as though she had been crying slowly and painfully, for hours.

'Oh, hello, Andy,' she said brokenly. 'I haven't seen you for so long. Has he gone?'

'Now, Ailie –'

'Now, Ailie!' she cried. 'Now, Ailie! He spoke to me, you see. He lifted his hat. He stood there ten feet from me with that horrible – that horrible woman – holding her arm and talking to her, and then when he saw me he raised his hat. Andy, I didn't know what to do. I had to go in the drug store and ask for a glass of water, and I was so afraid he'd follow in after me that I asked Mr Rich to let me go out the back way. I never want to see him or hear of him again.'

I talked. I said what one says in such cases. I said it for half an hour. I could not move her. Several times she answered by murmuring something about his not being 'sincere', and for the fourth time I wondered what the word meant to her. Certainly not constancy; it was, I half suspected, some special way she wanted to be regarded.

I got up to go. And then, unbelievably, the automobile horn sounded three times impatiently outside. It was stupefying. It said as plainly as if Earl were in the room, 'All right; go to the devil then! I'm not going to wait here all night.'

Ailie looked at me aghast. And suddenly a peculiar look came into her face, spread, flickered, broke into a teary, hysterical smile.

'Isn't he awful?' she cried in helpless despair. 'Isn't he terrible?'

'Hurry up,' I said quickly. 'Get your cape. This is our last night.'

And I can still feel that last night vividly, the candlelight that flickered over the rough boards of the mess shack, over the frayed paper decorations left from the supply company's party, the sad mandolin down a company street that kept picking *My Indiana Home* out of the universal nostalgia of the departing summer. The three girls lost in this mysterious men's city felt something, too – a bewitched impermanence as though they were on a magic carpet that had lighted on the Southern countryside, and any moment the wind would lift it and waft it away. We toasted ourselves and the South. Then we left our napkins and empty glasses and a little of the past on the table, and hand in hand went out into the moonlight itself. Taps had been played; there was no sound but the far-away whinny of a horse, and a loud persistent snore at which we laughed, and the leathery snap of a sentry coming to port over by the guardhouse. Craker was on duty; we others got into a waiting car, motored into Tarleton and left Craker's girl.

Then Ailie and Earl, Sally and I, two and two in the wide back seat, each couple turned from the other, absorbed and whispering, drove away into the wide, flat darkness.

We drove through pinewoods heavy with lichen and Spanish moss, and between the fallow cotton fields along a road white as the rim of the world. We parked under the broken shadow of a mill where there was the sound of running water and restive squawky birds and over everything a brightness that tried to filter in anywhere – into the lost nigger cabins, the automobile, the fastnesses of the heart. The South sang to us – I wonder if they remember. I remember – the cool pale faces, the somnolent amorous eyes and the voices:

'Are you comfortable?'

'Yes, are you?'

'Are you sure you are?'

'Yes.'

Suddenly we knew it was late and there was nothing more. We turned home.

Our detachment started for Camp Mills next day, but I didn't go to France after all. We passed a cold month on Long Island, marched aboard a transport with steel helmets slung at our sides and then marched off again. There wasn't any more war. I had missed the war. When I came back to Tarleton I tried to get out of the Army, but I had a regular commission and it took most of the winter. But Earl Schoen was one of the first to be demobilized. He wanted to find a good job 'while the picking was good'. Ailie was non-committal, but there was an understanding between them that he'd be back.

By January the camps, which for two years had dominated the little city, were already fading. There was only the persistent incinerator smell to remind one of all that activity and bustle. What life remained centred bitterly about divisional headquarters building with the disgruntled regular officers who had also missed the war.

And now the young men of Tarleton began drifting back from the ends of the earth – some with Canadian uniforms, some with crutches or empty sleeves. A returned battalion of the National Guard paraded through the streets with open ranks for their dead, and then stepped down out of romance for ever and sold you things over the counters of local stores. Only a few uniforms mingled with the dinner coats at the country-club dance.

Just before Christmas, Bill Knowles arrived unexpectedly one day and left the next – either he gave Ailie an ultimatum or she had made up her mind at last. I saw her sometimes when she wasn't busy with returned heroes from Savannah and Augusta, but I felt like an outmoded survival – and I was. She was waiting for Earl Schoen with such a vast uncertainty that she didn't like to talk about it. Three days before I got my final discharge he came.

I first happened upon them walking down Market Street together, and I don't think I've ever been so sorry for a couple in my life; though I suppose the same situation was repeating itself in every city where there had been camps. Exteriorly Earl had about everything wrong with him that could be imagined. His hat was green, with a radical feather;

his suit was slashed and braided in a grotesque fashion that national advertising and the movies have put an end to. Evidently he had been to his old barber, for his hair bloused neatly on his pink, shaved neck. It wasn't as though he had been shiny and poor, but the background of mill-town dance halls and outing clubs flamed out at you – or rather flamed out at Ailie. For she had never quite imagined the reality; in these clothes even the natural grace of that magnificent body had departed. At first he boasted of his fine job; it would get them along all right until he could 'see some easy money'. But from the moment he came back into her world on its own terms he must have known it was hopeless. I don't know what Ailie said or how much her grief weighed against her stupefaction. She acted quickly – three days after his arrival, Earl and I went North together on the train.

'Well, that's the end of that,' he said moodily. 'She's a wonderful girl, but too much of a highbrow for me. I guess she's got to marry some rich guy that'll give her a great social position. I can't see that stuck-up sort of thing.' And then, later: 'She said to come back and see her in a year, but I'll never go back. This aristocrat stuff is all right if you got the money for it, but –'

'But it wasn't real,' he meant to finish. The provincial society in which he had moved with so much satisfaction for six months already appeared to him as affected, 'dudish', and artificial.

'Say, did you see what I saw getting on the train?' he asked me after a while. 'Two wonderful janes, all alone. What do you say we mosey into the next car and ask them to lunch? I'll take the one in blue.' Halfway down the car he turned around suddenly. 'Say, Andy,' he demanded, frowning; 'one thing – how do you suppose she knew I used to command a street car? I never told her that.'

'Search me.'

III

This narrative arrives now at one of the big gaps that stared me in the face when I began. For six years, while I finished at Harvard Law and built commercial aeroplanes and backed a pavement block that went gritty under trucks, Ailie Calhoun was scarcely more than a name on a Christmas card; something that blew a little in my mind on warm nights when I remembered the magnolia flowers. Occasionally an acquaintance of Army days would ask me, 'What became of that blonde girl who was so popular?' but I didn't know. I ran into Nancy Lamar at the Montmartre in New York one evening and learned that Ailie had become engaged to a man in Cincinatti, had gone North to visit his family, and then broken it off. She was lovely as ever and there was always a heavy beau or two. But neither Bill Knowles nor Earl Schoen had ever come back.

And somewhere about that time I heard that Bill Knowles had married a girl he met on a boat. There you are – not much of a patch to mend six years with.

Oddly enough, a girl seen at twilight in a small Indiana station started me thinking about going South. The girl, in stiff pink organdie, threw her arms about a man who got off our train and hurried him to a waiting car, and I felt a sort of pang. It seemed to me that she was bearing him off into the lost midsummer world of my early twenties, where time had stood still and charming girls, dimly seen like the past itself, still loitered along the dusky streets. I suppose that poetry is a Northern man's dream of the South. But it was months later that I sent off a wire to Ailie, and immediately followed it to Tarleton.

It was July. The Jefferson Hotel seemed strangely shabby and stuffy – a boosters' club burst into intermittent song in the dining-room that my memory had long dedicated to officers and girls. I recognized the taxi driver who took me up to Ailie's house, but his 'Sure, I do, Lieutenant,' was unconvincing. I was only one of twenty thousand.

It was a curious three days. I suppose some of Ailie's first young lustre must have gone the way of such mortal shining, but I can't bear witness to it. She was still so physically appealing that you wanted to touch the personality that trembled on her lips. No – the change was more profound than that.

At once I saw she had a different line. The modulations of pride, the vocal hints that she knew the secrets of a brighter, finer ante-bellum day, were gone from her voice; there was no time for them now as it rambled on in the half-laughing, half-desperate banter of the newer South. And everything was swept into this banter in order to make it go on and leave no time for thinking – the present, the future, herself, me. We went to a rowdy party at the house of some young married people, and she was the nervous, glowing centre of it. After all, she wasn't eighteen, and she was as attractive in her rôle of reckless clown as she had ever been in her life.

'Have you heard anything from Earl Schoen?' I asked her the second night, on our way to the country-club dance.

'No.' She was serious for a moment. 'I often think of him. He was the –' she hesitated.

'Go on.'

'I was going to say the man I loved most, but that wouldn't be true. I never exactly loved him, or I'd have married him any old how, wouldn't I?' She looked at me questioningly. 'At least I wouldn't have treated him like that.'

'It was impossible.'

'Of course,' she agreed uncertainly. Her mood changed; she became flippant: 'How the Yankees did deceive us poor little Southern girls. Ah, me!'

When we reached the country club she melted like a chameleon into the – to me – unfamiliar crowd. There was a new generation upon the floor, with less dignity than the ones I had known, but none of them were more a part of its lazy, feverish essence than Ailie. Possibly she had perceived that in her initial longing to escape from Tarleton's provincialism she had been walking alone, following a generation which was doomed to have no successors. Just where she lost the battle, waged behind the white pillars of her veranda, I don't know. But she had guessed wrong, missed out somewhere. Her wild animation, which even now called enough men around her to rival the entourage of the youngest and freshest, was an admission of defeat.

I left her house, as I had so often left it that vanished June, in a mood of vague dissatisfaction. It was hours later, tossing about my bed in the hotel, that I realized what was the matter, what had always been the matter – I was deeply and incurably in love with her. In spite of every incompatibility, she was still, she would always be to me, the most attractive girl I had ever known. I told her so next afternoon. It was one of those hot days I knew so well, and Ailie sat beside me on a couch in the darkened library.

'Oh, no, I couldn't marry you,' she said, almost frightened; 'I don't love you that way at all. . . . I never did. And you don't love me, I didn't mean to tell you now, but next month I'm going to marry another man. We're not even announcing it, because I've done that twice before.' Suddenly it occurred to her that I might be hurt: 'Andy, you just had a silly idea, didn't you? You know I couldn't ever marry a Northern man.'

'Who is he?' I demanded.

'A man from Savannah.'

'Are you in love with him?'

'Of course I am.' We both smiled. 'Of course I am! What are you trying to make me say?'

There were no doubts, as there had been with other men. She couldn't afford to let herself have doubts. I knew this because she had long ago stopped making any pretensions with me. This very naturalness, I realized, was because she didn't consider me as a suitor. Beneath her mask of an instinctive thoroughbred she had always been on to herself, and she couldn't believe that anyone not taken in to the point of uncritical worship could really love her. That was what she called being 'sincere'; she felt most security with men like Canby and Earl Schoen, who were incapable of passing judgements on the ostensibly aristocratic heart.

'All right,' I said, as if she had asked my permission to marry. 'Now, would you do something for me?'

'Anything.'

'Ride out to camp.'

'But there's nothing left there, honey.'

'I don't care.'

We walked downtown. The taxi-driver in front of the hotel repeated her objection: 'Nothing there now, Cap.'

'Never mind. Go there anyhow.'

Twenty minutes later he stopped on a wide unfamiliar plain powdered with new cotton fields and marked with isolated clumps of pine.

'Like to drive over yonder where you see the smoke?' asked the driver. 'That's the new state prison.'

'No. Just drive along this road. I want to find where I used to live.'

An old racecourse, inconspicuous in the camp's day of glory, had reared its dilapidated grandstand in the desolation. I tried in vain to orient myself.

'Go along this road past that clump of trees, and then turn right – no, turn left.'

He obeyed, with professional disgust.

'You won't find a single thing, darling,' said Ailie. 'The contractors took it all down.'

We rode slowly along the margin of the fields. It might have been here –

'All right. I want to get out,' I said suddenly.

I left Ailie sitting in the car, looking very beautiful with the warm breeze stirring her long, curly bob.

It might have been here. That would make the company streets down there and the mess shack, where we dined that night, just over the way.

The taxi-driver regarded me indulgently while I stumbled here and there in the knee-deep underbrush, looking for my youth in a clapboard or a strip of roofing or a rusty tomato can. I tried to sight on a vaguely familiar clump of trees, but it was growing darker now and I couldn't be quite sure they were the right trees.

'They're going to fix up the old racecourse,' Ailie called from the car. 'Tarleton's getting quite doggy in its old age.'

No. Upon consideration they didn't look like the right trees. All I could be sure of was this place that had once been full of life and effort was gone, as if it had never existed, and that in another month Ailie would be gone, and the South would be empty for me for ever.

Babylon Revisited

'And where's Mr Campbell?' Charlie asked.

'Gone to Switzerland. Mr Campbell's a pretty sick man, Mr Wales.'

'I'm sorry to hear that. And George Hardt?' Charlie inquired.

'Back in America, gone to work.'

'And where is the Snow Bird?'

'He was in here last week. Anyway, his friend, Mr Schaeffer, is in Paris.'

Two familiar names from the long list of a year and a half ago. Charlie scribbled an address in his notebook and tore out the page.

'If you see Mr Schaeffer, give him this,' he said. 'It's my brother-in-law's address. I haven't settled on a hotel yet.'

He was not really disappointed to find Paris was so empty. But the stillness in the Ritz bar was strange and portentous. It was not an American bar any more – he felt polite in it, and not as if he owned it. It had gone back into France. He felt the stillness from the moment he got out of the taxi and saw the doorman, usually in a frenzy of activity at this hour, gossiping with a *chasseur* by the servants' entrance.

Passing through the corridor, he heard only a single, bored voice in the once-clamorous women's room. When he turned into the bar he travelled the twenty feet of green carpet with his eyes fixed straight ahead by old habit; and then, with his foot firmly on the rail, he turned and surveyed the room, encountering only a single pair of eyes that fluttered up from a newspaper in the corner. Charlie asked for the head barman, Paul, who in the latter days of the bull market had come to work in his own custom-built car – disembarking, however, with due nicety at the nearest corner. But Paul was at his country house today and Alix giving him information.

'No, no more,' Charlie said, 'I'm going slow these days.'

Alix congratulated him: 'You were going pretty strong a couple of years ago.'

'I'll stick to it all right,' Charlie assured him. 'I've stuck to it for over a year and a half now.'

'How do you find conditions in America?'

'I haven't been to America for months. I'm in business in Prague, representing a couple of concerns there. They don't know about me down there.'

Alix smiled.

'Remember the night of George Hardt's bachelor dinner here?' said Charlie. 'By the way, what's become of Claude Fessenden?'

Alix lowered his voice confidentially: 'He's in Paris, but he doesn't come here any more. Paul doesn't allow it. He ran up a bill of thirty thousand francs, charging all his drinks and his lunches, and usually his dinner, for more than a year. And when Paul finally told him he had to pay, he gave him a bad cheque.'

Alix shook his head sadly.

'I don't understand it, such a dandy fellow. Now he's all bloated up –' He made a plump apple of his hands.

Charlie watched a group of strident queens installing themselves in a corner.

'Nothing affects them,' he thought. 'Stocks rise and fall, people loaf or work, but they go on forever.' The place oppressed him. He called for the dice and shook with Alix for the drink.

'Here for long, Mr Wales?'

'I'm here for four or five days to see my little girl.'

'Oh-h! You have a little girl?'

Outside, the fire-red, gas-blue, ghost-green signs shone smokily through the tranquil rain. It was late afternoon and the streets were in movement; the *bistros* gleamed. At the corner of the Boulevard des Capucines he took a taxi. The Place de la Concorde moved by in pink majesty; they crossed the logical Seine, and Charlie felt the sudden provincial quality of the left bank.

Charlie directed his taxi to the Avenue de l'Opéra, which was out of his way. But he wanted to see the blue hour spread over the magnificent façade, and imagine that the cab horns, playing endlessly the first few bars of Le Plus que Lent, were the trumpets of the Second Empire. They were closing the iron grill in front of Brentano's Book-store, and people were already at dinner behind the trim little bourgeois hedge of Duval's. He had never eaten at a really cheap restaurant in Paris. Five-course dinner, four francs fifty, eighteen cents, wine included. For some odd reason he wished that he had.

As they rolled on to the Left Bank and he felt its sudden provincialism, he thought, 'I spoiled this city for myself. I didn't realize it, but the days came along one after another, and then two years were gone, and everything was gone, and I was gone.'

He was thirty-five, and good to look at. The Irish mobility of his face was sobered by a deep wrinkle between his eyes. As he rang his brother-in-law's bell in the Rue Palatine, the wrinkle deepened till it pulled down his brow; he felt a cramping sensation in his belly. From behind the maid who opened the door darted a lovely little girl of nine who shrieked 'Daddy!' and flew up, struggling like a fish into his arms. She pulled his head around by one ear and set her cheek against his.

'My old pie,' he said.

'Oh, daddy, daddy, daddy, daddy, dads, dads, dads!'

She drew him into the salon, where the family waited, a

boy and a girl his daughter's age, his sister-in-law and her husband. He greeted Marion with his voice pitched carefully to avoid either feigned enthusiasm or dislike, but her response was more frankly tepid, though she minimized her expression of unalterable distrust by directing her regard towards his child. The two men clasped hands in a friendly way and Lincoln Peters rested his for a moment on Charlie's shoulder.

The room was warm and comfortably American. The three children moved intimately about, playing through the yellow oblongs that led to other rooms; the cheer of six o'clock spoke in the eager smacks of the fire and the sounds of French activity in the kitchen. But Charlie did not relax; his heart sat up rigidly in his body and he drew confidence from his daughter, who from time to time came close to him, holding in her arms the doll he had brought.

'Really extremely well,' he declared in answer to Lincoln's question. 'There's a lot of business there that isn't moving at all, but we're doing even better than ever. In fact, damn well. I'm bringing my sister over from America next month to keep house for me. My income last year was bigger than it was when I had money. You see, the Czechs –'

His boasting was for a specific purpose; but after a moment, seeing a faint restiveness in Lincoln's eye, he changed the subject:

'Those are fine children of yours, well brought up, good manners.'

'We think Honoria's a great little girl too.'

Marion Peters came back from the kitchen. She was a tall woman with worried eyes, who had once possessed a fresh American loveliness. Charlie had never been sensitive to it and was always surprised when people spoke of how pretty she had been. From the first there had been an instinctive antipathy between them.

'Well, how do you find Honoria?' she asked.

'Wonderful. I was astonished how much she's grown in ten months. All the children are looking well.'

'We haven't had a doctor for a year. How do you like being back in Paris?'

'It seems very funny to see so few Americans around.'

'I'm delighted,' Marion said vehemently. 'Now at least you can go into a store without their assuming you're a millionaire. We've suffered like everybody, but on the whole it's a good deal pleasanter.'

'But it was nice while it lasted,' Charlie said. 'We were a sort of royalty, almost infallible, with a sort of magic around us. In the bar this afternoon' – he stumbled, seeing his mistake – 'there wasn't a man I knew.'

She looked at him keenly. 'I should think you'd have had enough of bars.'

'I only stayed a minute. I take one drink every afternoon, and no more.'

'Don't you want a cocktail before dinner?' Lincoln asked.

'I take only one drink every afternoon, and I've had that.'

'I hope you keep to it,' said Marion.

Her dislike was evident in the coldness with which she spoke, but Charlie only smiled; he had larger plans. Her very aggressiveness gave him an advantage, and he knew enough to wait. He wanted them to initiate the discussion of what they knew had brought him to Paris.

At dinner he couldn't decide whether Honoria was most like him or her mother. Fortunate if she didn't combine the traits of both that had brought them to disaster. A great wave of protectiveness went over him. He thought he knew what to do for her. He believed in character; he wanted to jump back a whole generation and trust in character again as the eternally valuable element. Everything else wore out.

He left soon after dinner, but not to go home. He was curious to see Paris by night with clearer and more judicious eyes than those of other days. He bought a *strapontin* for the Casino and watched Josephine Baker go through her chocolate arabesques.

After an hour he left and strolled towards Montmartre, up the Rue Pigalle into the Place Blanche. The rain had stopped and there were a few people in evening clothes disembarking from taxis in front of cabarets, and *cocottes* prowling singly or in pairs, and many Negroes. He passed a lighted door from which issued music, and stopped with the sense of familiarity; it was Bricktop's, where he had parted with so many hours and so much money. A few doors farther on he found another ancient rendezvous and incautiously put his head inside. Immediately an eager orchestra burst into sound, a pair of professional dancers leaped to their feet and a maître d'hôtel swooped towards him, crying, 'Crowd just arriving, sir!' But he withdrew quickly.

'You have to be damn drunk,' he thought.

Zelli's was closed, the bleak and sinister cheap hotels surrounding it were dark; up in the Rue Blanche there was more light and a local, colloquial French crowd. The Poet's Cave had disappeared, but the two great mouths of the Café of Heaven and the Café of Hell still yawned – even devoured, as he watched, the meagre contents of a tourist bus – a German, a Japanese, and an American couple who glanced at him with frightened eyes.

So much for the effort and ingenuity of Montmartre. All the catering to vice and waste was on an utterly childish scale, and he suddenly realized the meaning of the word 'dissipate' – to dissipate into thin air; to make nothing out of something. In the little hours of the night every move from place to place was an enormous human jump, an increase of paying for the privilege of slower and slower motion.

He remembered thousand-franc notes given to an orchestra for playing a single number, hundred-franc notes tossed to a doorman for calling a cab.

But it hadn't been given for nothing.

It had been given, even the most wildly squandered sum, as an offering to destiny that he might not remember the things most worth remembering, the things that now he would always remember – his child taken from his control, his wife escaped to a grave in Vermont.

In the glare of a *brasserie* a woman spoke to him. He bought her some eggs and coffee, and then, eluding her encouraging stare, gave her a twenty-franc note and took a taxi to his hotel.

II

He woke upon a fine fall day – football weather. The depression of yesterday was gone and he liked the people on the streets. At noon he sat opposite Honoria at Le Grand Vatel, the only restaurant he could think of not reminiscent of champagne dinners and long luncheons that began at two and ended in a blurred and vague twilight.

'Now, how about vegetables? Oughtn't you to have some vegetables?'

'Well, yes.'

'Here's *épinards* and *chou-fleur* and carrots and *haricots*.'

'I'd like *chou-fleur*.'

'Wouldn't you like to have two vegetables?'

'I usually only have one at lunch.'

The waiter was pretending to be inordinately fond of children.

'*Qu'elle est mignonne la petite! Elle parle exactement comme une Française*.'

'How about dessert? Shall we wait and see?'

The waiter disappeared. Honoria looked at her father expectantly.

'What are you going to do?'

'First, we're going to that toy store in the Rue Saint-Honoré and buy you anything you like. And then we're going to the vaudeville at the Empire.'

She hesitated. 'I like it about the vaudeville, but not the toy store.'

'Why not?'

'Well, you brought me this doll.' She had it with her. 'And I've got lots of things. And we're not rich any more, are we?'

'We never were. But today you are to have anything you want.'

'All right,' she agreed resignedly.

When there had been her mother and a French nurse he had been inclined to be strict; now he extended himself, reached out for a new tolerance; he must be both parents to her and not shut any of her out of communication.

'I want to get to know you,' he said gravely. 'First let me introduce myself. My name is Charles J. Wales, of Prague.'

'Oh, daddy!' her voice cracked with laughter.

'And who are you, please?' he persisted, and she accepted a rôle immediately: 'Honoria Wales, Rue Palatine, Paris.'

'Married or single?'

'No, not married. Single.'

He indicated the doll. 'But I see you have a child, madame.'

Unwilling to disinherit it, she took it to her heart and thought quickly: 'Yes, I've been married, but I'm not married now. My husband is dead.'

He went on quickly, 'And the child's name?'

'Simone. That's after my best friend at school.'

'I'm very pleased that you're doing so well at school.'

'I'm third this month,' she boasted. 'Elsie' – that was her cousin – 'is only about eighteenth, and Richard is about at the bottom.'

'You like Richard and Elsie, don't you?'

'Oh, yes. I like Richard quite well and I like her all right.'

Cautiously and casually he asked: 'And Aunt Marion and Uncle Lincoln – which do you like best?'

'Oh, Uncle Lincoln, I guess.'

He was increasingly aware of her presence. As they came in, a murmur of '. . . adorable' followed them, and now the people at the next table bent all their silences upon her, staring as if she were something no more conscious than a flower.

'Why don't I live with you?' she asked suddenly. 'Because mamma's dead?'

'You must stay here and learn more French. It would have been hard for daddy to take care of you so well.'

'I don't really need much taking care of any more. I do everything for myself.'

Going out of the restaurant, a man and a woman unexpectedly hailed him.

'Well, the old Wales!'

'Hello there, Lorraine. . . . Dunc.'

Sudden ghosts out of the past: Duncan Schaeffer, a friend from college. Lorraine Quarrles, a lovely, pale blonde of thirty; one of a crowd who had helped them make months into days in the lavish times of three years ago.

'My husband couldn't come this year,' she said, in answer to his question. 'We're poor as hell. So he gave me two hundred a month and told me I could do my worst on that. . . . This your little girl?'

'What about coming back and sitting down?' Duncan asked.

'Can't do it.' He was glad for an excuse. As always, he felt Lorraine's passionate, provocative attraction, but his own rhythm was different now.

'Well, how about dinner?' she asked.

'I'm not free. Give me your address and let me call you.'

'Charlie, I believe you're sober,' she said judicially. 'I honestly believe he's sober, Dunc. Pinch him and see if he's sober.'

Charlie indicated Honoria with his head. They both laughed.

'What's your address?' said Duncan sceptically.

He hesitated, unwilling to give the name of his hotel.

'I'm not settled yet. I'd better call you. We're going to see the vaudeville at the Empire.'

'There! That's what I want to do,' Lorraine said. 'I want to see some clowns and acrobats and jugglers. That's just what we'll do, Dunc.'

'We've got to do an errand first,' said Charlie. 'Perhaps we'll see you there.'

'All right, you snob. . . . Good-bye, beautiful little girl.'

'Good-bye.'

Honoria bobbed politely.

Somehow, an unwelcome encounter. They liked him because he was functioning, because he was serious; they wanted to see him, because he was stronger than they were now, because they wanted to draw a certain sustenance from his strength.

At the Empire, Honoria proudly refused to sit upon her father's folded coat. She was already an individual with a code of her own, and Charlie was more and more absorbed by the desire of putting a little of himself into her before she crystallized utterly. It was hopeless to try to know her in so short a time.

Between the acts they came upon Duncan and Lorraine in the lobby where the band was playing.

'Have a drink?'

'All right, but not up at the bar. We'll take a table.'

'The perfect father.'

Listening abstractedly to Lorraine, Charlie watched Honoria's eyes leave their table, and he followed them wistfully about the room, wondering what they saw. He met her glance and she smiled. 'I liked that lemonade,' she said.

What had she said? What had he expected? Going home

in a taxi afterwards, he pulled her over until her head rested against his chest.

'Darling, do you ever think about your mother?'

'Yes, sometimes,' she answered vaguely.

'I don't want you to forget her. Have you got a picture of her?'

'Yes, I think so. Anyhow, Aunt Marion has. Why don't you want me to forget her?'

'She loved you very much.'

'I loved her too.'

They were silent for a moment.

'Daddy, I want to come and live with you,' she said suddenly.

His heart leaped; he had wanted it to come like this.

'Aren't you perfectly happy?'

'Yes, but I love you better than anybody. And you love me better than anybody, don't you, now that mummy's dead?'

'Of course I do. But you won't always like me best, honey. You'll grow up and meet somebody your own age and go marry him and forget you ever had a daddy.'

'Yes, that's true,' she agreed tranquilly.

He didn't go in. He was coming back at nine o'clock and he wanted to keep himself fresh and new for the thing he must say then.

'When you're safe inside, just show yourself in that window.'

'All right. Good-bye, dads, dads, dads, dads.'

He waited in the dark street until she appeared, all warm and glowing, in the window above and kissed her fingers out into the night.

III

They were waiting. Marion sat behind the coffee service in a dignified black dinner dress that just faintly suggested mourning. Lincoln was walking up and down with the animation of one who had already been talking. They were as anxious as he was to get into the question. He opened it almost immediately:

'I suppose you know what I want to see you about – why I really came to Paris.'

Marion played with the black stars on her necklace and frowned.

'I'm awfully anxious to have a home,' he continued. 'And I'm awfully anxious to have Honoria in it. I appreciate your taking in Honoria for her mother's sake, but things have changed now' – he hesitated and then continued more forcibly – 'changed radically with me, and I want to ask you to reconsider the matter. It would be silly for me to deny that about three years ago I was acting badly –'

Marion looked up at him with hard eyes.

'– but all that's over. As I told you, I haven't had more than a drink a day for over a year, and I take that drink deliberately, so that the idea of alcohol won't get too big in my imagination. You see the idea?'

'No,' said Marion succinctly.

'It's a sort of stunt I set myself. It keeps the matter in proportion.'

'I get you,' said Lincoln. 'You don't want to admit it's got any attraction for you.'

'Something like that. Sometimes I forget and don't take it. But I try to take it. Anyhow, I couldn't afford to drink in my position. The people I represent are more than satisfied with what I've done, and I'm bringing my sister over from Burlington to keep house for me, and I want awfully to have Honoria too. You know that even when her mother and I weren't getting along well we never let anything that happened touch Honoria. I know she's fond of me and I know I'm able to take care of her and – well, there you are. How do you feel about it?'

He knew that now he would have to take a beating. It would last an hour or two hours, and it would be difficult, but if he modulated his inevitable resentment to the chastened attitude of the reformed sinner, he might win his point in the end.

Keep your temper, he told himself. You don't want to be justified. You want Honoria.

Lincoln spoke first: 'We've been talking it over ever since we got your letter last month. We're happy to have Honoria here. She's a dear little thing, and we're glad to be able to help her, but of course that isn't the question –'

Marion interrupted suddenly. 'How long are you going to stay sober, Charlie?' she asked.

'Permanently, I hope.'

'How can anybody count on that?'

'You know I never did drink heavily until I gave up business and came over here with nothing to do. Then Helen and I began to run around with –'

'Please leave Helen out of it. I can't bear to hear you talk about her like that.'

He stared at her grimly; he had never been certain how fond of each other the sisters were in life.

'My drinking only lasted about a year and a half – from the time we came over until I – collapsed.'

'It was time enough.'

'It was time enough,' he agreed.

'My duty is entirely to Helen,' she said. 'I try to think what she would have wanted me to do. Frankly, from the night you did that terrible thing you haven't really existed for me. I can't help that. She was my sister.'

'Yes.'

'When she was dying she asked me to look out for Honoria. If you hadn't been in a sanatorium then, it might have helped matters.'

He had no answer.

'I'll never in my life be able to forget the morning when Helen knocked at my door, soaked to the skin and shivering and said you'd locked her out.'

Charlie gripped the sides of the chair. This was more difficult than he expected; he wanted to launch out into a long expostulation and explanation, but he only said: 'The night I locked her out –' and she interrupted, 'I don't feel up to going over that again.'

After a moment's silence Lincoln said: 'We're getting off the subject. You want Marion to set aside her legal guardianship and give you Honoria. I think the main point for her is whether she has confidence in you or not.'

'I don't blame Marion,' Charlie said slowly, 'but I think she can have entire confidence in me. I had a good record up to three years ago. Of course, it's within human possibilities I might go wrong any time. But if we wait much longer I'll lose Honoria's childhood and my chance for a home.' He shook his head, 'I'll simply lose her, don't you see?'

'Yes, I see,' said Lincoln.

'Why didn't you think of all this before?' Marion asked.

'I suppose I did, from time to time, but Helen and I were getting along badly. When I consented to the guardianship, I was flat on my back in a sanatorium and the market had cleaned me out. I knew I'd acted badly, and I thought if it would bring any peace to Helen, I'd agree to anything. But now it's different. I'm functioning, I'm behaving damn well, so far as –'

'Please don't swear at me,' Marion said.

He looked at her, startled. With each remark the force of her dislike became more and more apparent. She had built up all her fear of life into one wall and faced it towards him. This trivial reproof was possibly the result of some trouble with the cook several hours before. Charlie became increasingly alarmed at leaving Honoria in this atmosphere of hostility against himself; sooner or later it would come out in a word here, a shake of the head there, and some of that distrust would be irrevocably implanted in Honoria. But he pulled his temper down out of his face and shut it up inside him; he had won a point, for Lincoln realized the absurdity of Marion's remark and asked her lightly since when she had objected to the word 'damn'.

'Another thing,' Charlie said: 'I'm able to give her certain advantages now. I'm going to take a French governess to Prague with me. I've got a lease on a new apartment –'

He stopped, realizing that he was blundering. They couldn't be expected to accept with equanimity the fact that his income was again twice as large as their own.

'I suppose you can give her more luxuries than we can,' said Marion. 'When you were throwing away money we were living along watching every ten francs. . . . I suppose you'll start doing it again.'

'Oh, no,' he said. 'I've learned. I worked hard for ten years, you know – until I got lucky in the market, like so many people. Terribly lucky. It won't happen again.'

There was a long silence. All of them felt their nerves straining, and for the first time in a year Charlie wanted a drink. He was sure now that Lincoln Peters wanted him to have his child.

Marion shuddered suddenly; part of her saw that Charlie's feet were planted on the earth now, and her own maternal feeling recognized the naturalness of his desire; but she had lived for a long time with a prejudice – a prejudice founded on a curious disbelief in her sister's happiness, and which, in the shock of one terrible night, had turned to hatred for him. It had all happened at a point in her life where the discouragement of ill health and adverse circumstances made it necessary for her to believe in tangible villainy and a tangible villain.

'I can't help what I think!' she cried out suddenly. 'How

much you were responsible for Helen's death, I don't know. It's something you'll have to square with your own conscience.'

An electric current of agony surged through him; for a moment he was almost on his feet, an unuttered sound echoing in his throat. He hung on to himself for a moment, another moment.

'Hold on there,' said Lincoln uncomfortably. 'I never thought you were responsible for that.'

'Helen died of heart trouble,' Charlie said dully.

'Yes, heart trouble.' Marion spoke as if the phrase had another meaning for her.

Then, in the flatness that followed her outburst, she saw him plainly and she knew he had somehow arrived at control over the situation. Glancing at her husband, she found no help from him, and as abruptly as if it were a matter of no importance, she threw up the sponge.

'Do what you like!' she cried, springing up from her chair. 'She's your child. I'm not the person to stand in your way. I think if it were my child I'd rather see her –' She managed to check herself. 'You two decide it. I can't stand this, I'm sick. I'm going to bed.'

She hurried from the room; after a moment Lincoln said:

'This has been a hard day for her. You know how strongly she feels –' His voice was almost apologetic: 'When a woman gets an idea in her head.'

'Of course.'

'It's going to be all right. I think she sees now that you – can provide for the child, and so we can't very well stand in your way or Honoria's way.'

'Thank you, Lincoln.'

'I'd better go along and see how she is.'

'I'm going.'

He was still trembling when he reached the street, but a walk down the Rue Bonaparte to the *quais* set him up, and as he crossed the Seine, fresh and new by the *quai* lamps, he felt exultant. But back in his room he couldn't sleep. The image of Helen haunted him. Helen whom he had loved so until they had senselessly begun to abuse each other's love, tear it into shreds. On that terrible February night that Marion remembered so vividly, a slow quarrel had gone on for hours. There was a scene at the Florida, and then he attempted to take her home, and then she kissed young Webb at a table; after that there was what she had hysterically said. When he arrived home alone he turned the key in the lock in wild anger. How could he know she would arrive an hour later alone, that there would be a snowstorm in which she wandered about in slippers, too confused to find a taxi? Then the aftermath, her escaping pneumonia by a miracle, and all the attendant horror. They were 'reconciled', but that was the beginning of the end, and Marion, who had seen with her own eyes and who imagined it to be one of many scenes from her sister's martyrdom, never forgot.

Going over it again brought Helen nearer, and in the white, soft light that steals upon half sleep near morning he found himself talking to her again. She said that he was perfectly right about Honoria and that she wanted Honoria to be with him. She said she was glad he was being good and doing better. She said a lot of other things – very friendly things – but she was in a swing in a white dress, and swinging faster and faster all the time, so that at the end he could not hear clearly all that she said.

IV

He woke up feeling happy. The door of the world was open again. He made plans, vistas, futures for Honoria and himself, but suddenly he grew sad, remembering all the plans he and Helen had made. She had not planned to die. The present was the thing – work to do and someone to love.

But not to love too much, for he knew the injury that a father can do to a daughter or a mother to a son by attaching them too closely: afterward, out in the world, the child would seek in the marriage partner the same blind tenderness and, failing probably to find it, turn against love and life.

It was another bright, crisp day. He called Lincoln Peters at the bank where he worked and asked if he could count on taking Honoria when he left for Prague. Lincoln agreed that there was no reason for delay. One thing – the legal guardianship. Marion wanted to retain that a while longer. She was upset by the whole matter, and it would oil things if she felt that the situation was still in her control for another year. Charlie agreed, wanting only the tangible, visible child.

Then the question of a governess. Charles sat in a gloomy agency and talked to a cross Béarnaise and to a buxom Breton peasant, neither of whom he could have endured. There were others whom he would see tomorrow.

He lunched with Lincoln Peters at Griffons, trying to keep down his exultation.

'There's nothing quite like your own child,' Lincoln said. 'But you understand how Marion feels too.'

'She's forgotten how hard I worked for seven years there,' Charlie said. 'She just remembers one night.'

'There's another thing.' Lincoln hesitated. 'While you and Helen were tearing around Europe throwing money away, we were just getting along. I didn't touch any of the prosperity because I never got ahead enough to carry anything but my insurance. I think Marion felt there was some kind of injustice in it – you not even working towards the end, and getting richer and richer.'

'It went just as quick as it came,' said Charlie.

'Yes, a lot of it stayed in the hands of *chasseurs* and saxophone players and maîtres d'hôtel – well, the big party's over now. I just said that to explain Marion's feeling about those crazy years. If you drop in about six o'clock tonight before Marion's too tired, we'll settle the details on the spot.'

Back at his hotel, Charlie found a *pneumatique* that had been re-directed from the Ritz bar where Charlie had left his address for the purpose of finding a certain man.

DEAR CHARLIE:

You were so strange when we saw you the other day that I wondered if I did something to offend you. If so, I'm not conscious of it. In fact, I have thought about you too much for the last year, and it's always been in the back of my mind that I might see you if I came over here. We *did* have such good times that crazy spring, like the night you and I stole the butcher's tricycle, and the time we tried to call on the president and you had the old derby rim and the wire cane. Everybody seems so old lately, but I don't feel old a bit. Couldn't we get together some time today for old time's sake? I've got a vile hang-over for the moment, but will be feeling better this afternoon and will look for you about five in the sweat-shop at the Ritz.

Always devotedly,

LORRAINE

His first feeling was one of awe that he had actually, in his mature years, stolen a tricycle and pedalled Lorraine all over the Étoile between the small hours and dawn. In retrospect it was a nightmare. Locking out Helen didn't fit in with any other act of his life, but the tricycle incident did – it was one of many. How many weeks or months of dissipation to arrive at that condition of utter irresponsibility?

He tried to picture how Lorraine had appeared to him then – very attractive; Helen was unhappy about it, though she said nothing. Yesterday, in the restaurant, Lorraine had seemed trite, blurred, worn away. He emphatically did not want to see her, and he was glad Alix had not given away his hotel address. It was a relief to think instead of Honoria, to think of Sundays spent with her and of saying good morning to her and of knowing she was there in his house at night, drawing her breath in the darkness.

At five he took a taxi and bought presents for all the Peters – a piquant cloth doll, a box of Roman soldiers, flowers for Marion, big linen handkerchiefs for Lincoln.

He saw, when he arrived in the apartment, that Marion had accepted the inevitable. She greeted him now as though he were a recalcitrant member of the family, rather than a menacing outsider. Honoria had been told she was going; Charlie was glad to see that her tact made her conceal her excessive happiness. Only on his lap did she whisper her delight and the question 'When?' before she slipped away with the other children.

He and Marion were alone for a minute in the room, and on an impulse he spoke out boldly:

'Family quarrels are bitter things. They don't go according to any rules. They're not like aches or wounds; they're more like splits in the skin that won't heal because there's not enough material. I wish you and I could be on better terms.'

'Some things are hard to forget,' she answered. 'It's a question of confidence.' There was no answer to this and presently she asked, 'When do you propose to take her?'

'As soon as I can get a governess. I hoped the day after tomorrow.'

'That's impossible. I've got to get her things in shape. Not before Saturday.'

He yielded. Coming back into the room, Lincoln offered him a drink.

'I'll take my daily whisky,' he said.

It was warm here, it was a home, people together by a fire. The children felt very safe and important; the mother and father were serious, watchful. They had things to do for the children more important than his visit here. A spoonful of medicine was, after all, more important than the strained relations between Marion and himself. They were not dull people, but they were very much in the grip of life and circumstances. He wondered if he couldn't do something to get Lincoln out of his rut at the bank.

A long peal at the doorbell; the *bonne à tout faire* passed through and went down the corridor. The door opened upon another long ring, and then voices, and the three in the salon looked up expectantly; Richard moved to bring the corridor within his range of vision, and Marion rose. Then the maid came back along the corridor, closely followed by the voices, which developed under the light into Duncan Schaeffer and Lorraine Quarrles.

They were gay, they were hilarious, they were roaring with laughter. For a moment Charlie was astounded; unable to understand how they ferreted out the Peters' address.

'Ah-h-h!' Duncan wagged his finger roguishly at Charlie. 'Ah-h-h!'

They both slid down another cascade of laughter. Anxious and at a loss, Charlie shook hands with them quickly and presented them to Lincoln and Marion. Marion nodded, scarcely speaking. She had drawn back a step towards the fire; her little girl stood beside her, and Marion put an arm about her shoulder.

With growing annoyance at the intrusion, Charlie waited for them to explain themselves. After some concentration Duncan said:

'We came to invite you out to dinner. Lorraine and I insist that all this shishi, cagey business 'bout your address got to stop.'

Charlie came closer to them, as if to force them backward down the corridor.

'Sorry, but I can't. Tell me where you'll be and I'll phone you in half an hour.'

This made no impression. Lorraine sat down suddenly on the side of a chair, and focusing her eyes on Richard, cried, 'Oh, what a nice little boy! Come here, little boy.' Richard glanced at his mother, but did not move. With a perceptible shrug of her shoulders, Lorraine turned back to Charlie:

'Come and dine. Sure your cousins won' mine. See you so sel'om. Or solemn.'

'I can't,' said Charlie sharply. 'You two have dinner and I'll phone you.'

Her voice became suddenly unpleasant. 'All right, we'll go. But I remember once when you hammered on my door at four A.M. I was enough of a good sport to give you a drink. Come on, Dunc.'

Still in slow motion, with blurred, angry faces, with uncertain feet, they retired along the corridor.

'Good night,' Charlie said.

'Good night!' responded Lorraine emphatically.

When he went back into the salon Marion had not moved, only now her son was standing in the circle of her other arm. Lincoln was still swinging Honoria back and forth like a pendulum from side to side.

'What an outrage!' Charlie broke out. 'What an absolute outrage!'

Neither of them answered. Charlie dropped into an armchair, picked up his drink, set it down again and said:

'People I haven't seen for two years having the colossal nerve –'

He broke off. Marion had made the sound 'Oh!' in one swift, furious breath, turned her body from him with a jerk and left the room.

Lincoln set down Honoria carefully.

'You children go in and start your soup,' he said, and when they obeyed, he said to Charlie:

'Marion's not well and she can't stand shocks. That kind of people make her really physically sick.'

'I didn't tell them to come here. They wormed your name out of somebody. They deliberately –'

'Well, it's too bad. It doesn't help matters. Excuse me a minute.'

Left alone, Charlie sat tense in his chair. In the next room he could hear the children eating, talking in monosyllables, already oblivious to the scene between their elders. He heard a murmur of conversation from a farther room and then the ticking bell of a telephone receiver picked up, and in a panic he moved to the other side of the room and out of earshot.

In a minute Lincoln came back. 'Look here, Charlie. I think we'd better call off dinner for tonight. Marion's in bad shape.'

'Is she angry with me?'

'Sort of,' he said, almost roughly. 'She's not strong and –'

'You mean she's changed her mind about Honoria?'

'She's pretty bitter right now. I don't know. You phone me at the bank tomorrow.'

'I wish you'd explain to her I never dreamed these people would come here. I'm just as sore as you are.'

'I couldn't explain anything to her now.'

Charlie got up. He took his coat and hat and started down the corridor. Then he opened the door of the dining-room and said in a strange voice, 'Good night, children.'

Honoria rose and ran around the table to hug him.

'Good night, sweetheart,' he said vaguely, and then trying to make his voice more tender, trying to conciliate something, 'Good night, dear children.'

V

Charlie went directly to the Ritz bar with the furious idea of finding Lorraine and Duncan, but they were not there, and he realized that in any case there was nothing he could do. He had not touched his drink at the Peters', and now he ordered a whisky-and-soda. Paul came over to say hello.

'It's a great change,' he said sadly. 'We do about half the business we did. So many fellows I hear about back in the States lost everything, maybe not in the first crash, but then in the second. Your friend George Hardt lost every cent, I hear. Are you back in the States?'

'No, I'm in business in Prague.'

'I heard that you lost a lot in the crash.'

'I did,' and he added grimly, 'but I lost everything I wanted in the boom.'

'Selling short.'

'Something like that.'

Again the memory of those days swept over him like a nightmare – the people they had met travelling; then people who couldn't add a row of figures or speak a coherent sentence. The little man Helen had consented to dance with at the ship's party, who had insulted her ten feet from the table; the women and girls carried screaming with drink or drugs out of public places –

– The men who locked their wives out in the snow, because the snow of twenty-nine wasn't real snow. If you didn't want it to be snow, you just paid some money.

He went to the phone and called the Peters' apartment; Lincoln answered.

'I called up because this thing is on my mind. Has Marion said anything definite?'

'Marion's sick,' Lincoln answered shortly. 'I know this thing isn't altogether your fault, but I can't have her go to pieces about it. I'm afraid we'll have to let it slide for six months; I can't take the chance of working her up to this state again.'

'I see.'

'I'm sorry, Charlie.'

He went back to his table. His whisky glass was empty,

but he shook his head when Alix looked at it questioningly. There wasn't much he could do now except send Honoria some things; he would send her a lot of things tomorrow. He thought rather angrily that this was just money – he had given so many people money. . . .

'No, no more,' he said to another waiter. 'What do I owe you?'

He would come back some day; they couldn't make him pay forever. But he wanted his child, and nothing was much good now, beside that fact. He wasn't young any more, with a lot of nice thoughts and dreams to have by himself. He was absolutely sure Helen wouldn't have wanted him to be so alone.

Pat Hobby Himself

A PATRIOTIC SHORT

Pat Hobby, the writer and the Man, had his great success in Hollywood during what Irvin Cobb refers to as 'the mosaic swimming-pool age – just before the era when they had to have a shin-bone of St Sebastian for a clutch lever'.

Mr Cobb no doubt exaggerates, for when Pat had his pool in those fat days of silent pictures, it was entirely cement, unless you should count the cracks where the water stubbornly sought its own level through the mud.

'But it *was* a pool,' he assured himself one afternoon more than a decade later. Though he was now more than grateful for this small chore he had assigned him by producer Berners – one week at two-fifty – all the insolence of office could not take that memory away.

He had been called in to the studio to work upon a humble short. It was based on the career of General Fitzhugh Lee, who fought for the Confederacy and later for the U.S.A. against Spain – so it would offend neither North nor South. And in the recent conference Pat had tried to cooperate.

'I was thinking –' he suggested to Jack Berners, '– that it might be a good thing if we could give it a Jewish touch.'

'What do you mean?' demanded Jack Berners quickly.

'Well, I thought – the way things are and all, it would be a sort of good thing to show that there were a number of Jews in it too.'

'In what?'

'In the Civil War.' Quickly he reviewed his meagre history. 'They were, weren't they?'

'Naturally,' said Berners, with some impatience. 'I suppose everybody was except the Quakers.'

'Well, my idea was that we could have this Fitzhugh Lee in love with a Jewish girl. He's going to be shot at curfew so she grabs a church bell –'

Jack Berners leaned forward earnestly.

'Say, Pat, you want this job, don't you? Well, I told you the story. You got the first script. If you thought up this tripe to please me you're losing your grip.'

Was that a way to treat a man who had once owned a pool which had been talked about by –

That was how he happened to be thinking about his long-lost swimming pool as he entered the shorts department. He was remembering a certain day over a decade ago in all its details, how he had arrived at the studio in his car driven by a Filipino in uniform; the deferential bow of the guard at the gate which had admitted car and all to the lot, his ascent to that long-lost office which had a room for the secretary and was really a director's office. . . .

His reverie was broken off by the voice of Ben Brown, head of the shorts department, who walked him into his own chambers.

'Jack Berners just phoned me,' he said. 'We don't want any new angles, Pat. We've got a good story. Fitzhugh Lee was a dashing cavalry commander. He was a nephew of Robert E. Lee and we want to show him at Appomattox, pretty bitter and all that. And then show how he became reconciled – we'll have to be careful because Virginia is swarming with Lees – and how he finally accepts a U.S. commission from President McKinley –'

Pat's mind darted back again into the past. The President – that was the magic word that had gone around that morning many years ago. The President of the United

States was going to make a visit to the lot. Everyone had been agog about it – it seemed to mark a new era in pictures, because a President of the United States had never visited a studio before. The executives of the company were all dressed up – from a window of his long-lost Beverly Hills house Pat had seen Mr Maranda, whose mansion was next door to him, bustle down his walk in a cutaway coat at nine o'clock, and had known that something was up. He thought maybe it was clergy, but when he reached the lot he had found it was the President of the United States himself who was coming . . .

'Clean up the stuff about Spain,' Ben Brown was saying. 'The guy that wrote it was a red and he's got all the Spanish officers with ants in their pants. Fix up that.'

In the office assigned him Pat looked at the script of *True to Two Flags*. The first scene showed General Fitzhugh Lee at the head of his cavalry receiving word that Petersburg had been evacuated. In the script Lee took the blow in pantomime, but Pat was getting two-fifty a week – so, casually and without effort, he wrote in one of his favourite lines:

LEE: (*to his officers*)

Well, what are you standing here gawking for? DO *something!*

6. *Medium Shot. Officers pepping up, slapping each other on back, etc.*

Dissolve to:

To what? Pat's mind dissolved once more into the glamorous past. On that happy day in the twenties his phone had rung at about noon. It had been Mr Maranda.

'Pat, the President is lunching in the private dining-room. Doug Fairbanks can't come so there's a place empty and anyhow we think there ought to be one writer there.'

His memory of the luncheon was palpitant with glamour.

The Great Man had asked some questions about pictures and had told a joke and Pat had laughed and laughed with the others – all of them solid men together – rich, happy and successful.

Afterwards the President was to go on some sets and see some scenes taken and still later he was going to Mr Maranda's house to meet some of the women stars at tea. Pat was not invited to that party but he went home early anyhow and from his veranda saw the cortège drive up, with Mr Maranda beside the President in the back seat. Ah, he was proud of pictures then – of his position in them – of the President of the happy country where he was born . . .

Returning to reality Pat looked down at the script of *True to Two Flags* and wrote slowly and thoughtfully: *Insert: A calendar – with the years plainly marked and the sheets blowing off in cold wind, to show Fitzhugh Lee growing older and older.*

His labours had made him thirsty – not for water, but he knew better than to take anything else his first day on the job. He got up and went out into the hall and along the corridor to the water-cooler.

As he walked he slipped back into his reverie.

That had been a lovely California afternoon, so Mr Maranda had taken his exalted guest and the coterie of stars into his garden, which adjoined Pat's garden. Pat had gone out his back door and followed a low privet hedge keeping out of sight – and then accidentally had come face to face with the Presidential party.

The President had smiled and nodded. Mr Maranda smiled and nodded.

'You met Mr Hobby at lunch,' Mr Maranda said to the President. 'He's one of our writers.'

'Oh, yes,' said the President. 'You write the pictures.'

'Yes, I do,' said Pat.

The President glanced over into Pat's property.

'I suppose,' he said, 'that you get lots of inspiration sitting by the side of that fine pool.'

'Yes,' said Pat. 'Yes, I do.'

. . . Pat filled his cup at the cooler. Down the hall there was a group approaching – Jack Berners, Ben Brown, and several other executives, and with them a girl to whom they were very attentive and deferential. He recognized her face – she was the girl of the year, the It Girl, the Oomph Girl, the Glamour Girl, the girl for whose services every studio was in violent competition.

Pat lingered over his drink. He had seen many phonies break in and break out again, but this girl was the real thing, someone to stir every pulse in the nation. He felt his own heart beat faster. Finally, as the procession drew near, he put down the cup, dabbed at his hair with his hand and took a step out into the corridor.

The girl looked at him – he looked at the girl. Then she took one arm of Jack Berners' and one of Ben Brown's and suddenly the party seemed to walk right through him – so that he had to take a step back against the wall.

An instant later Jack Berners turned around and said back to him, 'Hello, Pat.' And then some of the others threw half-glances around but no one else spoke, so interested were they in the girl.

In his office, Pat looked at the scene, where President McKinley offers a United States commission to Fitzhugh Lee. Suddenly he gritted his teeth and bore down on his pencil as he wrote:

LEE

Mr President, you can take your commission and go straight to hell.

Then he bent down over his desk, his shoulders shaking as he thought of that happy day when he had had a swimming pool.

TWO OLD-TIMERS

Phil Macedon, once the Star of Stars, and Pat Hobby, script writer, had collided out on Sunset near the Beverly Hills Hotel. It was five in the morning and there was liquor in the air as they argued and Sergeant Gaspar took them around to the station house. Pat Hobby, a man of forty-nine, showed fight, apparently because Phil Macedon failed to acknowledge that they were old acquaintances.

He accidentally bumped Sergeant Gaspar, who was so provoked that he put him in a little barred room while they waited for the captain to arrive.

Chronologically Phil Macedon belonged between Eugene O'Brien and Robert Taylor. He was still a handsome man in his early fifties and he had saved enough from his great days for a hacienda in the San Fernando Valley; there he rested as full of honours, as rollicksome and with the same purposes in life as Man o' War.

With Pat Hobby life had dealt otherwise. After twenty-one years in the industry, script and publicity, the accident found him driving a 1935 car which had lately become the property of the Acme Loan Co. And once, back in 1928, he had reached the point of having a private swimming pool.

He glowered from his confinement, still resenting Macedon's failure to acknowledge that they had ever met before.

'I suppose you don't remember Colman,' he said sarcastically. 'Or Connie Talmadge or Bill Corker or Allan Dwan.'

Macedon lit a cigarette with the sort of timing in which the silent screen has never been surpassed, and offered one to Sergeant Gaspar.

'Couldn't I come in tomorrow?' he asked. 'I have a horse to exercise –'

'I'm sorry, Mr Macedon,' said the cop – sincerely, for the actor was an old favourite of his. 'The captain is due here any minute. After that we won't be holding *you*.'

'It's just a formality,' said Pat, from his cell.

'Yeah, it's just a –' Sergeant Gaspar glared at Pat. 'It may not be any formality for *you*. Did you ever hear of the sobriety test?'

Macedon flicked his cigarette out the door and lit another.

'Suppose I come back in a couple of hours,' he suggested.

'No,' regretted Sergeant Gaspar. 'And since I have to detain you, Mr Macedon, I want to take the opportunity to tell you what you meant to me once. It was that picture you made, *The Final Push*, it meant a lot to every man who was in the war.'

'Oh, yes,' said Macedon, smiling.

'I used to try to tell my wife about the war – how it was, with the shells and the machine-guns – I was there seven months with the 26th New England – but she never understood. She'd point her finger at me and say "Boom! you're dead," and so I'd laugh and stop trying to make her understand.'

'Hey, can I get out of here?' demanded Pat.

'You shut up!' said Gaspar fiercely. 'You probably wasn't in the war.'

'I was in the Motion Picture Home Guard,' said Pat. 'I had bad eyes.'

'Listen to him,' said Gaspar disgustedly. 'That's what all them slackers say. Well, the war was *some*thing. And after my wife saw that picture of yours I never had to explain to her. She knew. She always spoke different about it after that – never just pointed her finger at me and said "Boom!" I'll never forget the part where you was in that shell-hole. That was so real it made my hands sweat.'

'Thanks,' said Macedon graciously. He lit another

cigarette. 'You see, I was in the war myself and I knew how it was. I knew how it felt.'

'Yes, sir,' said Gaspar appreciatively. 'Well, I'm glad of the opportunity to tell you what you did for me. You – explained the war to my wife.'

'What are you talking about?' demanded Pat Hobby suddenly. 'That war picture Bill Corker did in 1925?'

'There he goes again,' said Gaspar. 'Sure – *The Birth of a Nation*. Now you pipe down till the captain comes.'

'Phil Macedon knew me then all right,' said Pat resentfully. 'I even watched him work on it one day.'

'I just don't happen to remember you, old man,' said Macedon politely. 'I can't help that.'

'You remember the day Bill Corker shot that shell-hole sequence, don't you? Your first day on the picture?'

There was a moment's silence.

'When will the captain be here?' Macedon asked.

'Any minute now, Mr Macedon.'

'Well, I remember,' said Pat, 'because I was there when he had that shell-hole dug. He was out there on the back lot at nine o'clock in the morning with a gang of hunkies to dig the hole and four cameras. He called you up from a field telephone and told you to go to the costumer and get into a soldier suit. Now you remember?'

'I don't load my mind with details, old man.'

'You called up that they didn't have one to fit you and Corker told you to shut up and get into one anyhow. When you got out to the back lot you were sore as hell because your suit didn't fit.'

Macedon smiled charmingly.

'You have a most remarkable memory. Are you sure you have the right picture – and the right actor?' he asked.

'Am I!' said Pat grimly. 'I can see you right now. Only you didn't have much time to complain about the uniform because that wasn't Corker's plan. He always thought you were the toughest ham in Hollywood to get anything natural out of – and he had a scheme. He was going to get the heart of the picture shot by noon – before you even knew you were acting. He turned you around and shoved you down into that shell-hole on your fanny, and yelled "Camera".'

'That's a lie,' said Phil Macedon. 'I *got* down.'

'Then why did you start yelling?' demanded Pat. 'I can still hear you: "Hey, what's the idea! Is this some goddamn gag? You get me out of here or I'll walk out on you!"

'And all the time you were trying to claw your way up the side of that pit, so damn mad you couldn't see. You'd almost get up and then you'd slide back and lie there with your face working – till finally you began to bawl and all this time Bill had four cameras on you. After about twenty minutes you gave up and just lay there, heaving. Bill took a hundred feet of that and then he had a couple of prop men pull you out.'

The police captain had arrived in the squad car. He stood in the doorway against the first grey of dawn.

'What you got here, Sergeant? A drunk?'

Sergeant Gaspar walked over to the cell, unlocked it and beckoned Pat to come out. Pat blinked a moment – then his eyes fell on Phil Macedon and he shook his finger at him.

'So you see I *do* know you,' he said. 'Bill Corker cut that piece of film and titled it so you were supposed to be a doughboy whose pal had just been killed. You wanted to climb out and get at the Germans in revenge, but the shells bursting all around and the concussions kept knocking you back in.'

'What's it about?' demanded the captain.

'I want to prove I know this guy,' said Pat. 'Bill said the best moment in the picture was when Phil was yelling,

"I've already broken my first finger-nail!" Bill titled it, "Ten Huns will go to hell to shine your shoes!"'

'You've got here "collision with alcohol",' said the captain, looking at the blotter. 'Let's take these guys down to the hospital and give them the test.'

'Look here now,' said the actor, with his flashing smile, 'my name's Phil Macedon.'

The captain was a political appointee and very young. He remembered the name and the face, but he was not especially impressed because Hollywood was full of has-beens.

They all got into the squad car at the door.

After the test Macedon was held at the station house until friends could arrange bail. Pat Hobby was discharged, but his car would not run, so Sergeant Gaspar offered to drive him home.

'Where do you live?' he asked as they started home.

'I don't live anywhere tonight,' said Pat. 'That's why I was driving around. When a friend of mine wakes up I'll touch him for a couple of bucks and go to a hotel.'

'Well now,' said Sergeant Gaspar, 'I got a couple of bucks that ain't working.'

The great mansions of Beverly Hills slid by and Pat waved his hand at them in salute.

'In the good old days,' he said, 'I used to be able to drop into some of those houses day or night. And Sunday mornings –'

'Is that all true you said in the station,' Gaspar asked, '– about how they put him in the hole?'

'Sure, it is,' said Pat. 'That guy needn't have been so upstage. He's just an old-timer like me.'

Financing Finnegan

1

Finnegan and I have the same literary agent to sell our writings for us, but though I'd often been in Mr Cannon's office just before and just after Finnegan's visits, I had never met him. Likewise we had the same publisher and often when I arrived there Finnegan had just departed. I gathered from a thoughtful sighing way in which they spoke of him –

'Ah – Finnegan –'

'Oh yes, Finnegan was here.'

– that the distinguished author's visit had been not uneventful. Certain remarks implied that he had taken something with him when he went – manuscripts, I supposed, one of those great successful novels of his. He had taken 'it' off for a final revision, a last draft, of which he was rumoured to make ten in order to achieve that facile flow, that ready wit, which distinguished his work. I discovered only gradually that most of Finnegan's visits had to do with money.

'I'm sorry you're leaving,' Mr Cannon would tell me, 'Finnegan will be here tomorrow.' Then after a thoughtful pause, 'I'll probably have to spend some time with him.'

I don't know what note in his voice reminded me of a talk with a nervous bank president when Dillinger was reported in the vicinity. His eyes looked out into the distance and he spoke as to himself.

'Of course he may be bringing a manuscript. He has a novel he's working on, you know. And a play too.' He spoke as though he were talking about some interesting but remote events of the cinquecento; but his eyes became more hopeful as he added: 'Or maybe a short story.'

'He's very versatile, isn't he?' I said.

'Oh yes,' Mr Cannon perked up. 'He can do anything – anything when he puts his mind to it. There's never been such a talent.'

'I haven't seen much of his work lately.'

'Oh, but he's working hard. Some of the magazines have stories of his that they're holding.'

'Holding for what?'

'Oh, for a more appropriate time – an upswing. They like to think they have something of Finnegan's.'

His was indeed a name with ingots in it. His career had started brilliantly, and if it had not kept up to its first exalted level, at least it started brilliantly all over again every few years. He was the perennial man of promise in American letters – what he could actually do with words was astounding, they glowed and coruscated – he wrote sentences, paragraphs, chapters that were masterpieces of fine weaving and spinning. It was only when I met some poor devil of a screen writer who had been trying to make a logical story out of one of his books that I realized he had his enemies.

'It's all beautiful when you read it,' this man said disgustedly, 'but when you write it down plain it's like a week in the nut-house.'

From Mr Cannon's office I went over to my publishers on Fifth Avenue, and there too I learned in no time that Finnegan was expected tomorrow. Indeed he had thrown such a long shadow before him that the luncheon where I expected to discuss my own work was largely devoted to Finnegan. Again I had the feeling that my host, Mr George Jaggers, was talking not to me but to himself.

'Finnegan's a great writer,' he said.

'Undoubtedly.'

'And he's really quite all right, you know.'

As I hadn't questioned the fact I inquired whether there was any doubt about it.

'Oh, no,' he said hurriedly. 'It's just that he's had such a run of hard luck lately –'

I shook my head sympathetically. 'I know. That diving into a half-empty pool was a tough break.'

'Oh, it wasn't half-empty. It was full of water. Full to the brim. You ought to hear Finnegan on the subject – he makes a side-splitting story of it. It seems he was in a run-down condition and just diving from the side of the pool, you know –' Mr Jaggers pointed his knife and fork at the table, 'and he saw some young girls diving from the fifteen-foot board. He says he thought of his lost youth and went up to do the same and made a beautiful swan-dive – but his shoulder broke while he was still in the air.' He looked at me rather anxiously. 'Haven't you heard of cases like that – a ball player throwing his arm out of joint?'

I couldn't think of any orthopaedic parallels at the moment.

'And then,' he continued dreamily, 'Finnegan had to write on the ceiling.'

'On the ceiling?'

'Practically. He didn't give up writing – he has plenty of guts, that fellow, though you may not believe it. He had some sort of arrangement built that was suspended from the ceiling and he lay on his back and wrote in the air.'

I had to grant that it was a courageous arrangement.

'Did it affect his work?' I inquired. 'Did you have to read his stories backward – like Chinese?'

'They were rather confused for a while,' he admitted, 'but he's all right now. I got several letters from him that sounded more like the old Finnegan – full of life and hope and plans for the future –'

The far-away look came into his face and I turned the discussion to affairs closer to my heart. Only when we were back in his office did the subject recur – and I blush as I write this because it included confessing something I seldom do – reading another man's telegram. It happened because Mr Jaggers was intercepted in the hall and when I went into his office and sat down it was stretched out open before me:

With fifty I could at least pay typist and get haircut and pencils life has become impossible and I exist on dream of good news desperately. FINNEGAN

I couldn't believe my eyes – fifty dollars, and I happened to know that Finnegan's price for short stories was somewhere around three thousand. George Jaggers found me still staring dazedly at the telegram. After he read it he stared at me with stricken eyes.

'I don't see how I can conscientiously do it,' he said.

I started and glanced around to make sure I was in the prosperous publishing office in New York. Then I understood – I had misread the telegram. Finnegan was asking for fifty thousand as an advance – a demand that would have staggered any publisher no matter who the writer was.

'Only last week,' said Mr Jaggers disconsolately, 'I sent him a hundred dollars. It puts my department in the red every season, so I don't dare tell my partners any more. I take it out of my own pocket – give up a suit and a pair of shoes.'

'You mean Finnegan's broke?'

'Broke!' He looked at me and laughed soundlessly – in fact I didn't exactly like the way that he laughed. My brother had a nervous – but that is afield from this story. After a minute he pulled himself together. 'You won't say anything about this, will you? The truth is Finnegan's been in a slump, he's had blow after blow in the past few years, but now he's snapping out of it and I know we'll get back every cent we've –' He tried to think of a word but 'given him' slipped out. This time it was he who was eager to change the subject.

Don't let me give the impression that Finnegan's affairs absorbed me during a whole week in New York – it was inevitable, though, that being much in the offices of my agent and my publisher, I happened in on a lot. For instance, two days later, using the telephone in Mr Cannon's office, I was accidentally switched in on a conversation he was having with George Jaggers. It was only partly eavesdropping, you see, because I could only hear one end of the conversation and that isn't as bad as hearing it all.

'But I got the impression he was in good health . . . he did say something about his heart a few months ago but I understood it got well . . . yes, and he talked about some operation he wanted to have – I think he said it was cancer. . . . Well, I felt like telling him I had a little operation up my sleeve, too, that I'd have had by now if I could afford it. . . . No, I didn't say it. He seemed in such good spirits that it seemed a shame to bring him down. He's starting a story today, he read me some of it on the phone . . .

'. . . I did give him twenty-five because he didn't have a cent in his pocket . . . oh, yes – I'm sure he'll be all right now. He sounds as if he means business.'

I understood it all now. The two men had entered into a silent conspiracy to cheer each other up about Finnegan. Their investment in him, in his future, had reached a sum so considerable that Finnegan belonged to them. They could not bear to hear a word against him – even from themselves.

II

I spoke my mind to Mr Cannon.

'If this Finnegan is a four-flusher you can't go on indefinitely giving him money. If he's through he's through and there's nothing to be done about it. It's absurd that you should put off an operation when Finnegan's out somewhere diving into half-empty swimming pools.'

'It was full,' said Mr Cannon patiently – 'full to the brim.'

'Well, full or empty the man sounds like a nuisance to me.'

'Look here,' said Cannon, 'I've got a call from Hollywood due on the wire. Meanwhile you might glance over that.' He threw a manuscript into my lap. 'Maybe it'll help you understand. He brought it in yesterday.'

It was a short story. I began it in a mood of disgust, but before I'd read five minutes I was completely immersed in it, utterly charmed, utterly convinced, and wishing to God I could write like that. When Cannon finished his phone call I kept him waiting while I finished it and when I did there were tears in these hard old professional eyes. Any magazine in the country would have run it first in any issue.

But then nobody had ever denied that Finnegan could write.

III

Months passed before I went again to New York, and then, so far as the offices of my agent and my publisher were concerned, I descended upon a quieter, more stable world. There was at last time to talk about my own conscientious if uninspired literary pursuits, to visit Mr Cannon in the country, and to kill summer evenings with George Jaggers where the vertical New York starlight falls like lingering lightning into restaurant gardens. Finnegan might have been at the North Pole – and as a matter of fact he was. He had quite a group with him, including three Bryn Mawr anthropologists, and it sounded as if he might collect a lot of material there. They were going to stay several months, and if the thing had somehow the ring of a promising little house-party about it, that was probably due to my jealous, cynical disposition.

'We're all just delighted,' said Cannon. 'It's a godsend for him. He was fed up and he needed just this – this –'

'Ice and snow,' I supplied.

'Yes, ice and snow. The last thing he said was characteristic of him. Whatever he writes is going to be pure white – it's going to have a blinding glare about it.'

'I can imagine it will. But tell me – who's financing it? Last time I was here I gathered the man was insolvent.'

'Oh, he was really very decent about that. He owed me some money and I believe he owed George Jaggers a little too.' He 'believed', the old hypocrite. He knew damn well. 'So before he left he made most of his life insurance over to us. That's in case he doesn't come back – those trips are dangerous of course.'

'I should think so,' I said, 'especially with three anthropologists.'

'So Jaggers and I are absolutely covered in case anything happens – it's as simple as that.'

'Did the life-insurance company finance the trip?'

He fidgeted perceptibly.

'Oh, no. In fact when they learned the reason for the assignments they were a little upset. George Jaggers and I felt that when he had a specific plan like this with a specific book at the end of it, we were justified in backing him a little further.'

'I don't see it,' I said flatly.

'You don't?' The old harassed look came back into his eyes. 'Well, I'll admit we hesitated. In principle I know it's wrong. I used to advance authors small sums from time to time, but lately I've made a rule against it – and kept it. It's only been waived once in the last two years and that was for a woman who was having a bad struggle – Margaret Trahill, do you know her? She was an old girl of Finnegan's by the way.'

'Remember I don't even know Finnegan.'

'That's right. You must meet him when he comes back – if he does come back. You'd like him – he's utterly charming.'

Again I departed from New York, to imaginative North

Poles of my own, while the year rolled through summer and fall. When the first snap of November was in the air, I thought of the Finnegan expedition with a sort of shiver and any envy of the man departed. He was probably earning any loot, literary or anthropological, he might bring back. Then, when I hadn't been back in New York three days, I read in the paper that he and some other members of his party had walked off into a snowstorm when the food supply gave out, and the Arctic had claimed another sacrifice of intrepid man.

I was sorry for him, but practical enough to be glad that Cannon and Jaggers were well protected. Of course, with Finnegan scarcely cold – if such a simile is not too harrowing – they did not talk about it but I gathered that the insurance companies had waived *habeas corpus* or whatever it is in their lingo, just as if he had fallen overboard into the Atlantic, and it seemed quite sure that they would collect.

His son, a fine looking young fellow, came into George Jaggers' office while I was there and from him I could guess at Finnegan's charm – a shy frankness together with an impression of a very quiet, brave battle going on inside of him that he couldn't quite bring himself to talk about – but that showed as heat lightning in his work.

'The boy writes well too,' said George after he had gone. 'He's brought in some remarkable poems. He's not ready to step into his father's shoes, but there's a definite promise.'

'Can I see one of his things?'

'Certainly – here's one he left just as he went out.'

George took a paper from his desk, opened it and cleared his throat. Then he squinted and bent over a little in his chair.

'*Dear Mr Jaggers*,' he began, '*I didn't like to ask you this in person* –' Jaggers stopped, his eyes reading ahead rapidly.

'How much does he want?' I inquired.

He sighed.

'He gave me the impression that this was some of his work,' he said in a pained voice.

'But it is,' I consoled him. 'Of course he isn't quite ready to step into his father's shoes.'

I was sorry afterwards to have said this, for after all Finnegan had paid his debts, and it was nice to be alive now that better times were back and books were no longer rated as unnecessary luxuries. Many authors I knew who had skimped along during the depression were now making long-deferred trips or paying off mortgages or turning out the more finished kind of work that can only be done with a certain leisure and security. I had just got a thousand dollars advance for a venture in Hollywood and was going to fly out with all the verve of the old days when there was chicken feed in every pot. Going in to say good-bye to Cannon and collect the money, it was nice to find he too was profiting – wanted me to go along and see a motor-boat he was buying.

But some last-minute stuff came up to delay him and I grew impatient and decided to skip it. Getting no response to a knock on the door of his sanctum, I opened it anyhow.

The inner office seemed in some confusion. Mr Cannon was on several telephones at once and dictating something about an insurance company to a stenographer. One secretary was getting hurriedly into her hat and coat as upon an errand and another was counting bills from her purse upon a table.

'It'll be only a minute,' said Cannon, 'it's just a little office riot – you never saw us like this.'

'Is it Finnegan's insurance?' I couldn't help asking. 'Isn't it any good?'

'His insurance – oh, perfectly all right, perfectly. This is just a matter of trying to raise a few hundred in a hurry. The banks are closed and we're all contributing.'

'I've got that money you just gave me,' I said. 'I don't

need all of it to get to the coast.' I peeled off a couple of hundred. 'Will this be enough?'

'That'll be fine – it just saves us. Never mind, Miss Carlsen. Mrs Mapes, you needn't go now.'

'I think I'll be running along,' I said.

'Just wait two minutes,' he urged. 'I've only got to take care of this wire. It's really splendid news. Bucks you up.'

It was a cablegram from Oslo, Norway – before I began to read I was full of a premonition.

Am miraculously safe here but detained by authorities please wire passage money for four people and two hundred extra I am bringing back plenty greetings from the dead. FINNEGAN

'Yes, that's splendid,' I agreed. 'He'll have a story to tell now.'

'Won't he though,' said Cannon. 'Miss Carlsen, will you wire the parents of those girls – and you'd better inform Mr Jaggers.'

As we walked along the street a few minutes later, I saw that Mr Cannon, as if stunned by the wonder of this news, had fallen into a brown study, and I did not disturb him, for after all I did not know Finnegan and could not wholeheartedly share his joy. His mood of silence continued until we arrived at the door of the motor-boat show. Just under the sign he stopped and stared upward, as if aware for the first time where we were going.

'Oh, my,' he said stepping back. 'There's no use going in here now. I thought we were going to get a drink.'

We did. Mr Cannon was still a little vague, a little under the spell of the vast surprise – he fumbled so long for the money to pay his round that I insisted it was on me.

I think he was in a daze during that whole time because, though he is a man of the most punctilious accuracy, the two hundred I handed him in his office has never shown to my credit in the statements he has sent me. I imagine, though, that some day I will surely get it because some day Finnegan will click again and I know that people will clamour to read what he writes. Recently I've taken it upon myself to investigate some of the stories about him and I've found that they're mostly as false as the half-empty pool. That pool was full to the brim.

So far there's only been a short story about the polar expedition, a love story. Perhaps it wasn't as big a subject as he expected. But the movies are interested in him – if they can get a good long look at him first and I have every reason to think that he will come through. He'd better.

BY THE SAME AUTHOR

The Stories of
F. SCOTT FITZGERALD

VOLUME 1:
The Diamond as Big as the Ritz and Other Stories

A collection of his best short work. The title story is a symbolic fairy tale about unlimited wealth.

VOLUME 3:
The Pat Hobby Stories

As he hangs round Hollywood, Pat Hobby relives the golden days of his success, and the antics of this seedy, once talented charmer are both hilarious and sad.

VOLUME 4:
Bernice Bobs Her Hair and Other Stories

Full of contradictions and ironies – as well as the poignant dreams of youth – these eight short stories mirror life in the Jazz Age, and add sharply perceptive footnotes to Fitzgerald's own career.

VOLUME 5:
The Lost Decade and Other Stories

Six brilliant stories written at the heroic pitch of desperation in the last, twilight decade of Fitzgerald's life.

BY THE SAME AUTHOR

The Great Gatsby

No one ever rightly knew who Gatsby was. Some said that he had been a German spy, others that he was related to one of Europe's royal families. Despite this nearly everyone took advantage of his fabulous hospitality. And it really was fabulous. In his superb Long Island home he gave the most amazing parties, and not the least remarkable thing about them was the fact that few people could recognize their host. He seemed to be a person without background, without history, without a home. Yet the irony of this bright and brittle façade was that he had created it not to impress the world and his wife, but to impress just one person – a girl he had loved and had had to leave, a girl who had loved him but was now married to a rich good-for-nothing, a girl whom he had dreamed about for over four years. This dream had long ceased to have any substance or any connexion with reality – and for that reason he could not wake from it. He had doped himself with his own illusion. And only death could dispel that dream.

'It has interested and excited me more than any new novel I have seen, either English or American, for a number of years' – T. S. Eliot in a letter to the author in 1925

Also published:

THE LAST TYCOON

TENDER IS THE NIGHT

THIS SIDE OF PARADISE

THE BEAUTIFUL AND DAMNED